HOWL

New Irish Writing

23

New Irish Writing

CONTACT US:
HTTPS://HOWLWRITING.IE
HOWLWRITING@GMAIL.COM
@HOWLWRITING

EDITORS
Róisín Leggett Bohan
Lauren O'Donovan

EAGARTHÓIR GAEILGE
Ailbhe Ní Ghearbhuigh

GRAPHIC DESIGN
Michael Bohan

ASSISTANT EDITOR
May Quaid

Published in Cork, Ireland by *HOWL New Irish Writing*.
Printed by Walsh Colour Print, Ireland.
Cover design and layout by *HOWL New Irish Writing*.

Print edition: ISBN 978-1-9168905-5-8

HOWL New Irish Writing gratefully acknowledges
the support of Cork City Council.

Howl /haʊl/

noun

a call to family over a large area

CONTENTS

FICTION

NON-FICTION

POETRY

POETRY

ALL ROADS LEAD TO BALLINASLOE

CONOR MONTAGUE

I was four days into a meth binge, shooting pool with a one-legged dwarf in The Village Idiot on West 14th Street. The dwarf's name was Rosie. She turned tricks on 8th Avenue and hustled when business was slow. Rosie smelt of sandalwood and carried a blackthorn shillelagh which served as both walking aid and weapon. I was down sixty bucks, but it was worth it to watch her drag a beer crate round so she could shillelagh-vault up and shoot with her sawn-off cue. 'No tricks tonight?' I asked as I handed over another twenty. 'Not tonight, Three-Piece,' she said. 'Never did find no man wanted to ring in the new year with a one-legged dwarf.' 'Well, you found one now,' I said. 'Rack them up. Double or nothing.'

Hatchet and Olivia, my binge buddies, snorted a couple of key bumps and paid four dollars at the bar for two pints of goldfish. They fed the goldfish to the piranha, laughing maniacally each time they dropped one into the large turbulent tank by the front door. When out of goldfish, they perched on two stools, watched me and Rosie shoot pool, slammed tequilas, and squawked indecipherable instructions over Johnny Cash. A bunch of bikers had *San Quentin* on repeat. They necked Budweiser and arm wrestled as they sang along at the far end of the long narrow room. One shouldered me on his way to the bar, swung his bearded belligerence into my face. 'You ever do time in San Quentin?' he asked. 'You ever do time in Ballinasloe?' I answered and potted a solid. The biker stood in silent contemplation for some time, as if what I had said was incredibly profound. Perhaps it was. Who knew what passed for profound in The Village Idiot?

The evening was haunted by the lost souls of downtown. Hookers and shysters seeking respite from the bitter wind. Dealers blowing off steam after the last-minute rush. Loners worn down by solitude. All of us chancers at the last chance saloon. Towards midnight, we became aware of a suited man circling the room. He had an uptown look about him. Tailored threads and slicked-back hair. Feigned nonchalance diminished with each lap, his face gradually assuming the demeanour of a man being stalked by a malevolent spirit. Rosie eased up beside him and grabbed his hand. He turned to find nobody there and screamed. Rosie yanked his tie until he spotted her below. 'You looking for a good time, honey?'

Rosie had just sucked helium from one of the disinterested balloons which languished against the black ceiling. The man crumpled to his knees and burst into tears. Rosie pulled his face into her breasts, cackled a high-pitched cackle, and shimmied into him. 'I can't leave,' he cried, when she let him breathe. 'I can't find the door.' One of the bikers put *Hotel California* on the jukebox, and everybody in the room sang along and danced a clumsy jig around the fallen man as he descended deeper and deeper into horrific psychosis. On the third repeat of the track, I decided enough was enough and pulled the blubbering man-child to his feet. I led him through to the front bar, past the dominatrix whipping the bare arse of a moustached man, past the feeding frenzy in the piranha tank, past the cigar-chomping Latina bargirl and into the night.

The man gulped deep of the icy air, shot glances up and down the deserted street. I placed a hand on his shoulder. 'This isn't your world, my friend.' He looked up to where the neon sign blinked, *ILL ID*. 'I took a wrong turn.' 'We all take wrong turns,' I said. 'Those fiends in there just kept taking them.' He quietened. Settled into a pensive vibe. No doubt attempting to imagine what succession of wrong turns could lead to a place like The Village Idiot on New Year's Eve. The experience had broken something inside of him, shredded his uptown shield. He would never again strut through the doors of an unassuming bar on an unassuming street, would always fear the falsetto amputee dwarfs, the choral bikers, the ravenous piranha that lurked within.

A cab swung into the street from 7th Avenue. I waved it down and bundled the man into the back seat, threw the cabbie a twenty and told him to bring the man uptown. The man pressed his face to the window and stared at me until the cab crossed 8th Avenue. I followed its taillights until it turned right onto 9th before walking back into the bar. The stench of weed, whiskey, poppers, and stale beer hit like a damp putrid cloth after the night air. Rosie dished out tequilas she had bought with the cash from the man's wallet. 'I'm owed twenty,' I said. 'I'll play you for it, honey.'

'Okay. Rack them up.' It was almost midnight. The bikers chose *Life in the Fast Lane* to ring in the new year. We threw back shots and sang along as Rosie did back flips around the room, pogoing off her one leg like a crazed munchkin. We had counted down to one when Rosie misjudged a flip and cracked her head off the pool table. Olivia screeched, 'Tonight we're going to party like it's 1999,' her meth-mangled face towards the ceiling. The rest of us gathered around an unconscious Rosie, looking down on her as we would at a deformed new-born, none of us knowing quite what to say.

Alicia came out from behind the bar and joined our circle, exhaled a plume of cigar smoke onto the prone dwarf. 'She dead?' I hunkered down and placed two fingers on Rosie's sweaty neck. 'No,' I said and rolled Rosie face down. Her scalp was cut, but the bleeding wasn't serious. 'Anybody got any medical training?' I asked. 'Gruff is a doctor,' said one of the bikers, pointing at the man who had shouldered me. 'You a doctor, Gruff?' 'Yeah,' he said. 'What kind of doctor are you?' 'Philosophy. I have a PhD from Berkeley.' 'Thank God for that. If there is one,' said Hatchet, and laughed himself into a coughing fit. Olivia lurched forward and handed me a wrap. 'What's that for?' 'To wake her up. Blow some meth up her nose.' 'Maybe we should call an ambulance,' said Gruff. 'Fuck that,' said Alicia. 'An ambulance means cops.' 'Fuck that,' we all agreed.

Me and Hatchet hoisted Rosie onto the pool table. Alicia fetched a thick straw from behind the bar, snipped it in two with her cigar cutter and handed it to me. I stuffed a bump of meth into the straw with my bank card, crushed it on the edge of the table, inserted the straw into Rosie's left nostril and blew hard. We all stood around the pool table and watched, the first silence of the night. Hatchet grabbed Rosie's wrist and counted down seconds on an imaginary watch. Olivia mounted the pool table, squinted down at Rosie's cherub face. Thirty seconds later, Rosie's eyes shot open and she lurched upwards like a woman defibrillated, knocking Olivia off the table. 'Muthafucka.' Rosie glared at us, snorting through flared nostrils. Olivia scrambled to her feet, skirt hitched up her spindly legs, right side of her face caked in grime from the manky carpet. She nodded at me as if she had just successfully tested a cure for cancer. Gruff and Hatchet hoisted Rosie off the pool table and placed her on her foot. She stood swaying, scanning the room with lemur eyes until she located her blackthorn shillelagh to one side of the pool table. She hopped around the table, retrieved her stick, and turned to the bikers. 'Which one of you muthafuckas dry-gulched me?' Rosie vaulted forward and cracked the skull of the nearest biker, a monstrosity with a confederate flag tattooed just below his neckline. He slumped onto the floor, taking out two tables as he fell. Gruff ducked the next swipe. The rest scattered. Rosie pursued them around the room swinging her shillelagh with each hop, bottles and glasses smashing in her wake. Olivia fled into the front bar, horrified at the monster created by her meth experiment. I collapsed next to Hatchet in a corner, both of us incapacitated by hysterical laughter. Alicia sidled along the wall and stood over us. 'Get that crazy bitch outta here. *Ahora!*'

I grabbed Rosie from behind. Hatchet snatched her shillelagh and between us, we wrestled Rosie out the door and into the sub-minus smog which now filled the streets and avenues. I was struggling to position Rosie so she couldn't kick back into my balls when Gruff emerged from the bar and grabbed my arm. 'Tell me, man. How bad was Ballinasloe?' I tightened my hold on the crazed one-legged dwarf in my arms and looked him dead in the eye. 'Honestly? Makes this place look like kindergarten.' Gruff watched after us as we dragged Rosie into the thick fog, lost in imaginings of Ballinasloe, thanking the biker Gods he never did time there.

We got Rosie back to our ramshackle two-bed on Bleeker Street, threw three benzos into her and sat on her until she passed out. The apartment was freezing. Olivia stomped around, pissed because she needed a shower and there was no hot water. We assured her we'd sort it and stumbled down into the basement. Hatchet smacked himself on the forehead as we approached the boiler. 'Fuck's sake. The oil. We forgot the fucking oil.' The two of us had been on our way to order heating oil when we scored the meth. We sat by the parched boiler and smoked a spliff. 'No chance of sorting any today,' I said. Hatchet toked deep, exhaled a succession of pungent rings towards the cladded ceiling. 'Yeah. Well, we have to think of something. Olivia'll go fucking gaga if there's no heat.' We snorted a couple of bumps to kickstart our stalled brains. Hatchet leapt to his feet. 'I have a plan,' he said, and bolted up the stairs.

ALL ROADS LEAD TO BALLINASLOE

I finished the spliff before following, fearful of any light-bulb moment sparked into being by a bump of meth. Olivia swung towards me as I entered the room. 'Disney World, Three-Piece. Hatchet's bringing us to Disney World.' I look to Hatchet. 'Disney World? Florida?' 'No. Disney World, Alabama. Course it's Florida, dipshit.' Olivia jumped up and down, clapping her hands. 'It's New Year's Eve every night at Disney World. Did you know that, Three-Piece?' 'There's no way we'll be allowed onto a flight in this state,' I said. 'You two need to look in a mirror.' 'We're driving,' said Hatchet. 'Driving? It's a thousand miles. We haven't slept in four days.' 'We can do one more day,' he said, as if days were served in shot glasses. 'We have half an ounce of meth, a bag of weed, a tank full of gas.' 'We're not the fucking Blues Brothers.' I shouted, hoping my raised voice would puncture the fantasy. Olivia cracked into deranged laughter, ghoulish with her pallid dirt-caked face and gigantic pupils. 'It's a twenty-four-hour drive,' I said, lowering my voice this time so my pitch for sanity might seem credible. Hatchet consulted his imaginary watch. 'We can do it in twenty.' He consulted his wrist once more. 'I reckon we do five four-hour shifts between us.' 'And what if we get pulled over?' 'It'll be fine. I'm sober.' 'Yeah, he's sober. You're a fucking buzz kill, Three-Piece.' 'What about Rosie? We can't just leave her here.' 'We'll take her with us,' said Hatchet. 'Yeah, we'll take her home, man.' 'Olivia, Rosie lives in Brooklyn.' 'She lives in Brooklyn, but she's from Disney World. All dwarfs are from Disney World, man.' Olivia looked to Hatchet, exasperated by my ignorance. 'Hatchet,' I said, 'will you tell her, or will I?' 'She's right. It'll be good to have Rosie in the car if we get pulled over. We can tell the cops we're returning a dwarf to Disney World. Nobody's going to fuck with Disney World. They'll just wave us on.' It was futile to argue against this logic. We were driving to Florida.

We gathered drugs, cash, clothes, and Rosie's shillelagh. We were unable to rouse Rosie, and didn't want to risk the meth remedy, so I rolled her in a duvet, slung her over my shoulder, and carried her to the parking garage. When we arrived at Hatchet's battered Chevrolet Impala, Olivia refused to share the back seat with Rosie. 'I look like fucking Snow White to you? That crazy bitch freaks me out.' The security guard stepped out of his kiosk when he heard the commotion. I asked Hatchet to pop the trunk and placed Rosie inside. Hatchet threw the security guard a twenty as we reached the exit. 'It's okay,' he shouted, 'we're returning a dwarf to Disney World. Happy New Year.' We screeched out of the parking garage, turned right onto 12th Avenue, took the Lincoln Tunnel to New Jersey and headed south on the turnpike. I put a Digweed Ibiza mix on at full volume and sparked up a spliff. 'This is great,' said Hatchet. 'Best idea ever.'

We drove south, passing Philly, Baltimore, DC, into Maryland, sticking to four-hour shifts, one driving, one navigating. We took a pitstop every changeover and did a key bump every thirty minutes. It took two hours to convince Olivia to drop a benzo, another hour for it to kick in. The resultant tranquillity was bliss. We switched the soundtrack to Miles Davis and floated through Virginia, into North Carolina as dusk cast long shadows over the landscape. We'd just pulled out of a truck stop outside of Fayetteville when Hatchet checked the rear-view mirror. 'Shades.' I turned around to see a Highway Patrol car riding our tail. 'Will we make a run for it?' asked Hatchet, his tone that of a man suggesting a scenic shortcut. 'Make a run for it? Where the fuck will we run to? Play it cool, for fuck's sake.' 'I'm cool as Fonzy,' said Hatchet, 'I'll just tell them we're bringing a dwarf back to Disney World.' 'Jesus, we forgot about Rosie. How long has she been in the trunk?' Hatchet consulted his wrist. 'Not long. She'll be fine.' 'Not long? It's been about twelve fucking hours. She's probably dead.' 'Let's hope not. She's our ticket out of here if these pig fucks pull us over.' 'Don't tell them about Rosie.' 'Why the fuck not?' 'They hate dwarfs, down here.' 'I thought it was blacks they hated.' 'They hate dwarfs as well.' 'What about black dwarfs?' 'They'd have no chance.'

Hatchet shook his head and whistled, taken aback by the prejudice prevalent in these here parts. He turned to me, eyes bulging, face gaunt in the half-light. 'Grab Olivia's handbag.' 'You want to powder your nose or something?' 'Perfume, dipshit. Need to clear the stench of weed.' I reached back and plucked Olivia's handbag from her lap. Sirens and flashing lights behind as I rummaged through it and retrieved a bottle of *eau de cologne*. 'Fucking cannabis scented. What kind of crazy bitch has cannabis scented *eau de cologne*?' 'She's quite the ticket,' said Hatchet and sniggered. 'I'll open the windows.' He hit the switch. Smoke billowed from both sides of the car as Hatchet pulled up on the shoulder. The squad car swung in behind. Its flashing lights scorched our dehydrated eyeballs. A torch-bearing officer waddled alongside the car, free hand poised over his sidearm. A bloated midriff filled the window before a flushed face peered in, torch beam resting briefly on an unconscious Olivia before settling on the handbag on my knees. Modus operandi: abduction.

'How's it goin', officer?' chirped Hatchet, his elbow out the window, a man shooting the breeze with an old friend. 'Y'all Irish?' asked a nasal drawl. 'We sure are,' said Hatchet. 'Well, ain't that a doozy? I'm Irish. Where y'all from?' 'Galway.' 'Well, ain't that a doozy? My folks are from Galway. My Granddaddy was John Keady from Ballinasloe. You folks know Ballinasloe?' 'Yeah. We both spent time there.' 'Y'all don't mean the loony bin, I hope.' The three of us laughed long and hard, Hatchet slapped the steering wheel, overcome with mirth. 'Wouldn't that be a doozy?' asked the officer when our laughter subsided. 'I know the Keadys,' said Hatchet. 'Good hurlers.' 'You know the Keadys? Well, ain't that a doozy?' 'I'll tell them you said hello.' 'I sure would appreciate that. You tell them John Michael Patrick Keady says howdy. Y'all driving from Boston?' 'New York. Ran out of heating oil. Decided to head south to Orlando. See Disney World.' Officer John Michael Patrick Keady guffawed long and hard. He bent over and poked his swollen head into the car, into the stench of weed, above the white powder sprinkled across Hatchet's crotch. His voice lowered to a whisper. 'Y'all aware that there's no firearms in Disney World?' 'No,' I answered. 'I didn't know that.' He turns his face towards Hatchet, close enough to kiss. 'Not even security. Now, ain't that a doozy?' 'That sure is a doozy,' I said, hoping to draw his attention from Hatchet, who was liable to bite the nose off John Michael Patrick's flushed face if he didn't pull back. 'Especially with those dwarfs on the loose.' That drew his attention alright. I had no intention of bringing dwarfs into the conversation. The words left my mouth before I could spot them and rein them in. John Michael Patrick stared at me. 'We don't take to dwarfs round these here parts.' Hatchet nodded. 'Can't be trusted.' 'That ain't maybe,' said John Michael Patrick. 'Shoot you quick as look at you.' He looked at each of us in turn before extracting his head from the car. He straightened up and slapped the roof. 'You folks have a safe journey now, you hear?' Thanks, officer. We'll be sure to say hello to the Keadys.' 'I'd sure appreciate that.' He waddled back to his patrol car. It pulled out and headed down the highway, lights flashing. We watched it speed away. 'Fuck me,' said Hatchet. 'How weird was that?' 'What the fuck's a doozy?' I asked. 'Fucked if I know.' Hatchet consults his wrist. 'We'll have to make up time. Fancy a bump?'

It was past 3 a.m. when we pulled into a Days Inn motel on International Drive. We flopped out of the car, mangled. The air was a crisp summer night cool. Frogs whirred nearby, and the champagne perfume of magnolia infused the faint breeze. We each did a bump to straighten ourselves out. I checked us in to adjacent rooms while Hatchet attempted to rouse Olivia. When I arrived back with the key cards, Olivia was sitting on the bonnet, face on her like a bag of Gurkha knives. 'What the fuck are we doing in Orlando?' 'We're going to Disney World,' answered Hatchet. 'Fuck Disney World. Who the fuck wants to go to Disney World?' I handed Hatchet their key cards. 'Our rooms are around the back, ground floor.'

Hatchet popped the trunk so we could grab our bags. Rosie lay face up, eyes shut, mouth agape, neck crisscrossed with dried spittle. 'Rosie. We forgot Rosie. She's fucking dead.' Hatchet checked his imaginary watch. 'She's fine.' I placed my hand on her neck. Warm. With a pulse. Olivia slapped Hatchet across the face. 'You fucking Rosie, you piece of shit?' Hatchet and Olivia clawed at one another while I plucked Rosie from the trunk and threw her over my shoulder. I grabbed my bag and her shillelagh and headed across the parking lot. 'I'm going to bed. See you two in a few hours.'

A heated outdoor pool lay steaming about twenty metres from our rooms. At its edge, a blue heron stood one-legged, gazing into the up-lit water. I opened the door, laid Rosie on one of the beds and skinned up with trembling hands. I was jittery, wracked with shakes and spasms. Hatchet and Olivia burst into the adjacent room, screaming at one another. I needed sleep but couldn't take a benzo until Rosie woke. If she came to in an Orlando motel with me unconscious on the bed, there was a good chance she'd beat me to death with her shillelagh. Thumps from next door as Oliva threw shit at Hatchet. I decided on a night swim. Anything to get away from the madness, work the meth out of my system.

I'd forgotten to bring trunks so stripped naked and eased into the pool's warm embrace, the water silk on my skin as I swam slow lengths under the watchful eye of the heron. The jitters slowly dissipated as I swam, turning onto my back occasionally to gaze at the clear night sky, the indifferent stars, the clumped pointed leaves of the orange trees which lined one side of the pool. I emerged refreshed into the cool air, sat on a sun lounger to dry off, and sparked up. I was kicked back, naked, spliff in hand, when a gigantic pick-up truck screeched into the car park, mounted the kerb, demolished a sapling, and skidded to a halt about four inches from my bare feet. A Latino man leapt from the driver's seat, slammed the door, and headed towards the motel. 'Hey, asshole!' He swung around, glowered at me over the pistol in his right hand. A naked Irishman stretched out smoking a spiff on a cold winter night was obviously not something he had allowed for when he visualised his arrival at the motel. He was hyped on something. Epileptic eyes struggled to relay the scene to his brain. His face twitched with the effort.

I slowly brought the spliff to my lips and toked, allowing him time to settle. His deranged glare followed the spliff, strayed to my crotch. The cold wasn't doing me any favours. 'You mind not pointing that hand cannon at my face?' 'Who the fuck are you?' 'Who the fuck are you? You nearly ran me over, you gomey.' 'What are you doing out here? In this cold?' 'I don't feel the cold.' 'You Irish?' 'Yeah. You want a hit?' I stand. He lowers the gun and accepts the spliff. I grab my towel and wrap it around my waist. 'I'm Three-Piece.' 'Jesús.' He takes a hit. 'What you doing chilling out here, bro?' 'My friend and his girl were fighting. Brain was fried... You planning to shoot someone with that thing?' 'My fiancée.' 'That might spoil the wedding.' 'There ain't gonna be no wedding, bro.' He hands over the spliff, slumps onto the end of my sun-lounger. 'She up there with another man?' 'My friend.' 'He ain't no friend,' I said. Jesús contemplated a small lizard at his feet for a moment before nodding. 'And she ain't no fiancé,' I continued, 'not anymore.' Tears splashed onto the tiles, startling the lizard. It darted beneath a shrub. I fumbled into my clothes. The lizard emerged, tentative, tongue-flicked a teardrop.

'So, you're going to do a life sentence for a woman who's not your fiancé and a man who's not your friend?' 'Who says I'll get caught?' 'Your pickup's on camera entering the car park at high speed. There's cameras outside the rooms. We're probably on camera right now, you with a gun in your hand.' He stares at the gun, thumb shifting the safety.

'Listen, I'm not saying not to kill those two fucks, maybe they got it coming. I'm saying that you serving life without parole defeats the purpose. Why should you lose your life?' 'Maybe I don't care, bro.' 'You'll care. When that door slams shut behind you, you'll care.' He slipped the safety off, pointed the gun at his face, peered into the barrel. Tears plopped onto the gun, trickled onto a trembling hand. 'Not to mention the fact you'll be deaf.' He lowered the gun, turned to me. 'You ever shoot a .357 in an enclosed space?' Jesús shakes his head. 'That thing'll blow out your eardrums, man. You'll be deaf for weeks. Those pieces are for movies, or warzones, or rednecks on shooting ranges with ear protectors and polaroid glasses who imagine they're blasting away at *hombres*. No offence.' 'None taken.' 'And they kick like a riled jackass. You'd probably fire a round and drop the fucking thing.'

He held the gun at arm's length, panned along the top of the border hedge. 'All I'm saying is, that gun's the wrong tool for this particular job.' 'You know a lot about firearms?' 'I know enough.' 'Where'd you do time?' 'Ballinasloe.' 'Where's Ballinasloe?' 'In another lifetime.' Jesús placed the gun on the lounger, put his face in his hands, wiped his tears. 'What the fuck are you, bro? A leprechaun or some shit?' 'I'm no leprechaun. I have one in my room, though.' 'Now you're fucking with me.' I placed a hand on his shoulder. 'You know a place where we can get a beer?' 'Yeah. I know a place.' 'Does it have a pool table?' 'Yeah. It has a pool table.' 'How about we do a deal. Give me five minutes to run to my room and change my clothes, and if I come back here with a leprechaun, we'll all go for a beer and forget about shooting those two fucks.' 'How do I know you won't call the cops?' Do I look like somebody who's going to call the cops?' Jesús eyed me up and down. 'You look worse than I do, bro.' 'Yeah, it's been a long day.' I grabbed the towel and shoes and made for the room. Jesús hissed. I turned to face him. 'Hey bro. You believe in fate?' 'Do I fuck.' Jesús smiled. A gigantic wide-ass smile that shone luminescent in the pre-dawn gloom.

There was no smile on Rosie when I entered the room to find her hopping from the ensuite wrapped in a white towel. The TV was on, an advert for the local Ripley's Believe It or Not! museum. She grabbed her shillelagh. 'Three-Piece, you muthafucka. What the fuck am I doing in Orlando? And why's my head split like a cantaloupe?' 'Long story.'

'Yeah, well it better be one kicking muthafucka of a story.' Rosie hopped towards me, shillelagh raised. The towel fell from her as she backed me into a corner. I maintained eye contact. 'You up for a hussle?' 'What the fuck you talking about?' 'I found a place. Easy pickings.' 'It's near five a.m.' 'I've a friend waiting outside. He'll drive us there.' Rosie shapes to strike. 'You lying muthafucka. You ain't got no friend outside.' 'Seriously. My friend, Jesús. He's waiting in the parking lot. C'mon. Let's go shoot some pool.' She relaxed her grip, lowered the shillelagh. Her right breast flopped down as she did so. 'Would you mind not staring at my tits?' 'I wasn't.' 'I'm looking at you.' 'I am now. Cause you brought attention to them. Listen, Jesús is in a hurry. We can discuss breast etiquette when we get to the bar.' 'You got any meth?'

Jesús couldn't have looked more shocked if I'd walked out hand in wing with an ostrich. He stared at Rosie after I hoisted her into the middle seat. 'What the fuck are you gawking at?' 'Jesús, this is Rosie.' 'You weren't shitting me, bro.' 'No. I wasn't shitting you. Let's go have that beer.' We mounted two curbs and knocked a *Drive Slowly* sign before exiting onto International Drive. I lost count of the number of times Rosie screamed 'Muthafucka' as we swerved through traffic, past lines of motels, diners, and tourist tack. Jesús pointed out minor attractions, speaking in a soft rhythm so at odds with his driving I became convinced we'd been killed instantly in a head on collision and were now in an ever-recurring loop where a psychotic saviour informs us that Wet and Wild is indeed wet and wild again and again until the end of time.

Jesús swung into a small unlit parking lot. Aside from a line of Harleys, the lot was deserted. As we pulled up to one side of the motor-cycles, a bulky figure emerged from the shadows holding what looked to be a sawn-off shotgun. Jesús greeted him with a chirpy 'Hey, bro' as he leapt from the cab but obviously wasn't worthy of a response. I swung Rosie down from her seat and followed Jesús to a steel door set between two barred windows. An acrid stench seeped from garbage skips lined along the walls on either side. Jesús rapped on the door, smiled at me like a man who had just brought us to an exclusive Oscars after-party in Beverly Hills. A narrow shutter slid back at eye height, clunked shut. Rosie poked me. 'I feel like we're in a Scorsese movie. About to get whacked' 'It's cool,' I said. 'Trust me.' 'Trust you? Last time I had a drink with you I woke up a thousand miles away in a fucking motel room.' 'I told you. There's a perfectly reasonable explanation for that.' 'Yeah? I can't wait to hear that story.' The door opened into a narrow hallway lit by a single red bulb. *Smoke on the Water* blared from within. Jesús led us past a bearded doorman, through a musty corridor with storerooms on either side, into a long windowless room with two pool tables at the far end. High-back booths lined one wall, facing a bar counter, along which stagnated a spangled selection of drooped loners watching reruns of the weekend's basketball on mute. In one booth, three cackling sex workers sat around an overflowing ashtray, downing shots. In the next, a rugged bald man in combat fatigues nursed a beer as he watched the room. Two booths up, a bag lady ate yoghurt with a plastic fork. A bunch of bikers with Banditos patches were shooting pool. A pungent cloud of marijuana smoke clung to a low ceiling, hazing the room. 'Three-Piece, you muthafucka. You found The Village Idiot of Orlando.' 'Told you to trust me.' 'Fuck you. Bring me a tequila.' Rosie pogoed over to the pool tables, hyped on the line of meth she'd snorted back in the room. It was almost worth the thousand-mile drive to see the facial expressions of the Banditos when Rosie slapped a dollar bill marker on a table.

A bartender appeared from below the counter as I approached, a lithe Latina woman with collagen lips and a flattened nose. '*Hola*. Four shots of tequila in a Slim Jim with two cubes of ice and a slice of lime. And two beers.' 'What kind of beer?' I pointed to where Jesús was chatting to the man who had let us in. 'Whatever Jesús drinks.' Two frosted bottles of Corona were plucked from a cooler and placed on paper napkins. She twisted the caps off before scooping two cubes of ice into a Slim Jim, adding a chunk of lime and free pouring the Tequila. I threw thirty bucks onto the counter and brought the tequila down to Rosie. The baiting was well underway. One Bandito told a brother to forfeit his turn and 'Let the little lady shoot.' 'Who the fuck you calling little lady, you hairy piece of shit? I ain't no fucking lady.' The Banditos were laughing as I handed Rosie her drink. One grabbed an elbow on my way back to Jesús. He was about as stoned as a man could be and remain upright. 'Hey, friend. That your midget?' 'She's a dwarf.' 'She your dwarf?' 'She belongs to Disney World.' 'No shit?' 'No shit. Escaped a couple of months ago. Lost her leg to a 'gator crossing the swamp at night.' 'That's some radical shit, friend. Radical shit.' I leaned between fronds of hair which hung like curtains over a weather worn face. 'Keep it to yourself, my friend. Can't have word get out.' 'I hear you, friend. I hear you.'

Jesús was waiting for me at the counter. 'Hey, Maria. *Mi cabrón*, Three-Piece. *Chido. Él es Irlandés.*' The bartender eyed me as she sparked up a blunt. '*Mi abuelito estaba Irlandés.*' 'No shit! Hear that, Three-Piece? Maria's granddaddy was Irish.' Jesús was so pumped one might have thought Irishmen abroad were a scarce commodity. Maria erupted into rapid Spanish. Turned out Maria's grandaddy's granddaddy was a national hero, an Irish immigrant who had fought for Mexico against America in the 1840s. Second in command to John Riley from Galway. '*Mundo pequeño,*' I said and smiled at Maria. Fatigue was kicking in. I needed a bump. I looked towards the booths and caught a death stare from the rugged bald man. His face looked like it had been hewn from teak with a blunt stone. 'Jesús. The dude over there. What's his story?' Jesús looked at the man and waved. 'That's The Chief, bro. My soul brother, a real live hero right there.' 'Yeah?' 'Hell, yeah! Purple hearts, medals, that *hombre* did four tours in Vietnam, bro. *Mucho peligroso.* We sit with him, yes?'

I followed Jesús across to the booth. As we sat, The Chief leaned forward and punched Jesús bang on the chin. Jesús crumpled onto the floor, unconscious. I leaned down and put him into recovery position before sitting again. 'I take it that was your gun he took.' 'That's one dumb son of a bitch. He do any damage?' 'I talked him out of it.' 'Sounds like I owe you. Where's the piece?' 'Must be out in the truck.' He slid from the booth, took the keys from Jesús's pocket, and strode to the back door. I snuck a bump and watched Rosie reel in the Banditos. Looking for a crate, a short cue, the usual routine to sucker men into throwing dollar bills on the table. The Chief arrived back with two beers, placed one in front of me, and sat down with back to wall. 'I'm Three-Piece.' 'Uku,' he said and shook my hand. A deep bullet scar ran the length of a Popeye forearm. He looked to the bikers, gathered laughing around Rosie. One emerged from behind the bar, dropped to one knee, and presented her with a beer crate. 'The dwarf. She on the hustle?' 'Yeah.' 'You on a cut?' 'She does her own thing. Think I lose more to her than anybody.'

We watch Rosie's performance. The dragging of the crate, the vault, the seemingly clumsy shot, the lucky pot, the dollar bills landing on the table as all bet against her luck holding out. Uku looks over at me. 'How'd you end up with a name like Three-Piece?' 'Long story.' 'We in a hurry or something?' 'You know what holy Communion is?' 'My mother was Catholic, Irish/Mexican.' 'I grew up in an institution.' 'What kind of institution?' 'An orphanage. When I was eight, I was farmed out to a foster family, the Muldoons, just in time for my first holy Communion. Mrs Muldoon decided to dress me up in a three-piece suit for my big day. All the boys were dressed up. Shirt, tie, jacket or whatever. But I was the only one with a waistcoat. I've been known as Three-Piece ever since.' Uku laughed long and hard, body convulsing as he struggled for breath. 'Man, that's some crazy shit. You mean to tell me you've been called Three-Piece since you were eight years old cause you wore a waist-coat?' 'Ireland's like that. Once you get a nickname, it sticks.' 'That must be thirty years?' 'Twenty-nine. Could be worse. She could have dressed me in a frilly blouse.' 'That's a pretty inauspicious start to family life.' 'Didn't end too well either. They signed me into another institution when I was fifteen.'

Jesús stirred on the floor, slowly climbed to his feet, took a few moments to focus on the two of us. 'Hey, Uku. Think I blacked out.' 'It's been a long night, *migo*. Maybe you should lie up for a while.' 'Yeah. Think I might do that.' Jesús stumbles into the next booth and flops down onto the seat. 'You hit him pretty hard.' 'Not really. The candy he was smoking last night wore off, that's all.' 'How'd you end up with a name like The Chief?' 'That's my name. Uku is Cherokee for chief. My daddy's side of the family. He had high hopes for me.' 'An Irish/Mexican mother and Cherokee father. Good fighting pedigree.' 'All I've ever been good at.' He took a moment to size me up. 'What are you good at?' 'Surviving.' 'I buy that. Not every man could survive Jesús on a candy rampage.' 'He wanted a way out. I gave it to him. He said you served in Nam.' 'Spent a little time there.' 'That why you can't sleep?' 'Who says I can't sleep?' 'It's past five a.m. and you're drinking alone in the last chance saloon.' 'I can't sleep when my piece is in the hands of a loco Mexican. Had to wait until that motherfucker showed up.' Uku went quiet, scanned the room, watched the Banditos cheer on Rosie as she shaped to pot the black. I waved to Maria and she placed two beers on the counter. I grabbed them and returned to the table, quickly checking on Jesús before sitting down.

'I don't sleep either.' 'You're high on meth, *migo*.' 'That obvious?' 'Might want to wipe the powder ring from your nostril.' I whip a paper napkin from the table dispenser and wipe my nose. 'I mean in general.' 'I know what you mean.' Uku reached into an inside pocket and took out a short pipe and a baggie of weed. He loaded the bowl, sparked a brass Zippo and took a hit. He pushed the makings across the table to me, watched as I repeated the process. 'What has you in Orlando?' 'Took a wrong turn in New York.' 'Took it pretty fast, I reckon. How long you been high?' 'This is day five, I think. Or maybe six. What day is today?' 'Sunday. You might want to sober up if you're going to church.' 'This is church enough for me right now.' 'I hear you, *migo*. The sacred herb will redeem us.' Uku loaded his pipe and took another hit. The bag lady from two booths up appeared, an apparition through his exhaled smoke, clutching her plastic fork like it was the Olympic torch. She looked about eighty, scrawny with a hooked nose and stooped posture. 'Hey Uku. You got any pot to spare?' Uku extracted a couple of buds from his baggie, wrapped them in a paper napkin, and handed it to her. 'God bless you, Uku. Happy New Year.' Uku slid across the seat and took the woman in his arms. 'Happy New Year, Gert.' He released her and slid back. Gert pointed her plastic fork at him. '1999 is going to be our year, Uku. I can feel it in my bones.' She turned and hobbled back to her booth. 'What's her story?' 'She took a wrong turn.' He waved at Maria. We sat in silence until she brought our beers to the table and returned to the bar. 'The thing about wrong turns is that you don't know they're wrong when you take those motherfuckers.' 'Amen to that,' I said. We clinked bottles. 'Fucking amen to that.'

Time curled in on itself as we kicked back into the haze to a soundtrack of classic rock and unruly Banditos. We were shaken from our stupor when Rosie hopped over for a bump. I introduced her to Uku. 'You look like one mean muthafucka. No offence.' 'None taken.' 'Don't worry, honey. I'd still fuck you.' 'That's a weight off my mind, lil lady.' Rosie snorted her bump, shouted 'Muthafucka' and shook her shoulders. 'You want to go back to the motel, soon?' 'Fuck no. I ain't going nowhere. I'm fifteen hundred up and it's not even sunrise.' She bounced back to the Banditos. 'C'mon, you hairy-ass pieces of shit. Someone has to give me a game.' Uku chuckled. I snuck a bump, offered him the baggie. He shook his head. 'Done my time with that shit in Nam.' 'How long?' 'Three tours between sixty-seven and seventy-one.' 'Shit deal.' 'That ain't maybe.' 'Different place now.' 'You travelled the region?' 'Yeah. I'm over a couple of times a year. Vietnam, Cambodia, Thailand.' Uku smiles. 'What are you exporting?' 'At the moment, Viagra.' 'You're shitting me?' 'It's twenty-five a pop in Ireland. I can buy it in Phnom Penh for a dollar a pop.' 'The same pills?' 'Indian knockoffs but the same drug. No patent laws in India.' 'Why don't you buy them in India?' 'You ever been to India?' 'Can't say that I have.' 'Southeast Asia is a more enjoyable place to do business.' 'How much you sell the pills for?' 'I sell them for between twenty and twenty-five.' 'You're shitting me.' 'Seriously. Availability isn't the issue. Anyone can get them, but nobody wants to go to the doctor and say they can't get it up.' 'What about distribution?' 'My mate's a dealer. He offers them with his other produce, takes five per pill. On average, I clear thirteen to fifteen per tablet after expenses.' 'Man. That's sweet.' 'It won't last forever. Eventually you'll be able to buy that shit over the counter. Keeps me in funds for now, though.' 'What kind of bulk?' 'Took five thousand home last trip. Takes a while to shift, between sixty and eighty per week at the moment, but building all the time.' Uku's brow wrinkled as he did the arithmetic in his head. 'There's a lot of women in Galway who owe me a debt of gratitude. I'll give you my contact if you want.' 'Yeah?' 'Yeah. Not like I'll be bringing the love to Florida. You got a pen?' Uku rummages in a pocket and presents me with an ornate hand-crafted fountain pen. I twirl it in my fingers. 'Nice pen.' 'I like to write.' I tear a napkin from the dispenser and scribble down the details. 'My man's name is Makara. Tell him you're a friend of Three-Piece. I've included my number. If there's any problem, get in contact and I'll vouch for you.' I hand Uku the napkin. He folds it, places it in his breast pocket. 'I sure appreciate that. Could do with a vacation.' 'You shifting weed?' 'A little.' 'Mexico?' 'Mostly my own. I've got me a patch out in the swamp. Getting wild down south. Motherfuckers gone gun crazy. Bringing down all kinds of heat.'

We took another hit and settled into an easy silence. The intro to *Shine On You Crazy Diamond* was licking the frayed edges of my consciousness when Uku leaned into me. 'When were you diagnosed, *migo*?' 'Four years back. They were treating me for sleep apnoea, 'cause I was waking up choking, you know, not able to breathe.' 'I hear you, *migo*.' 'Nothing did any good, must have been years without a night's sleep.'

'How'd you get diagnosed?' 'Regressive hypnotherapy.' 'You're shitting me?' 'Turned out I was reliving a repressed memory.' 'Yeah? From when?' 'From when I was institutionalised.' 'I take it, it wasn't napalm you were choking on?' 'No. It wasn't napalm.' Rosie vaulted onto the seat. 'Bump me, muthafucka.' We both snorted a bump. 'I need to crash, Rosie.' 'I ain't goin' nowhere. This place is one sweet deal.' 'You're going to stay in Orlando?' 'Maybe I will. Who the fuck knows? You hit the highway, Three-Piece. I'll catch you up down the road a ways.' Rosie kissed me on the cheek, patted my crotch, and swung down off the seat. I watched her hop back to the Banditos, the clack of her shillelagh on the tiled floor contributing off-tempo beats to the music. Uku placed his pipe in a jacket pocket and stood. 'You want a ride back to your motel?'

Hatchet and Olivia were sat outside amongst a bunch of pasty tourists when we roared into the motel lot on a 1300cc Fat Boy. I hopped off the pillion seat and fist bumped Uku. 'Later, *migo*,' he said and took off, exhaust cracking like a Gatling gun as he pulled out onto International Drive and sped back towards town. I assumed a nonchalant air and turned to Hatchet and an open-mouthed Olivia. 'Howye.' 'Where were you?' asked Hatchet, looking around at the gathered hicks, self-conscious of what he must look like among the tourists. 'Went for a beer.' 'Yeah? Where?' 'Downtown.' Olivia punches me in the arm. 'We thought you'd crashed, man. Couldn't get no answer when we knocked on the door, like.' She was saucer-eyed, squawking at me. 'Who's the lad on the bike? Looks like fucking Mike Tyson, man.' 'Uku. He's a mate of mine.' Hatchet wasn't having any of it, knew he'd missed out on an adventure. As he shaped to interrogate me, a Disney shuttle bus pulled up and Olivia dragged him onto it. 'C'mon, man. We'll catch him later, like.' I walked to the room, flopped onto the bed, smiled at the thought of Hatchet spending his entire day at Disney obsessing about what he might have missed. 'It's the simple pleasures,' I mumbled as sleep washed over me. 'It's the simple pleasures.'

Galway. Sprawled stoned across my couch. Watching replays of the twin towers come down. Urgent knocking at the front door. Olivia. Obviously traumatised by events in New York. 'Three-Piece. Have you heard?' 'I'm watching it on TV. Come in.' She followed me into the room as they reran footage of the second plane striking the south tower. It's a long shot this time. We stood silent before the screen for a moment. 'Not this. Hatchet.' 'What about him?' 'He's banged up in Surat Thani.' 'Fuck off.' 'Seriously, one of the Thais ratted him out. Shades raided when they were packing the weed.' 'Fuck's sake. Were you talking to him?' 'Last night. He has a deal done with the shades. Twenty in sterling and he cuts them in on the scam. I have it here.' Olivia opened her handbag and bundled £20,000 in English notes onto the coffee table. She placed a smaller wad to one side, along with a white envelope. 'Two grand for expenses, and a one-way ticket to Bangkok. You'll have to book the return for both of you that side. Might look suspicious if you're only staying a few days.' 'Jesus, Olivia. I can't go to Bangkok. I'm up to my eyes.' 'You have to. Hatchet said it had to be you.' I opened the envelope and checked the ticket. 'Tomorrow morning? I need more time than that.' 'There is no time. It has to be sorted in the next three days. He's done a deal with the two that arrested him. Once the regional commander gets back, all bets are off. Hatchet will be sent to the Bangkok Hilton. He'll get twenty years, Three-Piece.' 'The flights are probably grounded.' 'The flight to Bangkok is still going. I checked.' 'Security will be a nightmare. They'll be searching everyone.' Olivia slumped onto the couch and burst into tears.

The following night I was mooching through the humid cacophonic chaos of Khaosan Road with a small rucksack over my shoulder and £20,000 strapped to my midriff, paranoid as a one-eyed meerkat in heavy mist, suspicious of every smile from every bargirl, every street vendor. I knew Hatchet hadn't slipped my name, aside from saying Three-Piece on the call to Olivia, but his new business partners could monitor Irish passengers arriving to Bangkok, watch buses and trains to Surat Thani. They could pull me in, take the money, throw both of us into the Bangkok Hilton. Why would they bother? They knew I'd be walking into that police station with the cash. What if one double-crossed the others? Planned to take all of the money for himself?

I spotted Lucky Beer ahead on the right, decided to grab a drink, calm my nerves before heading for the South Terminal to catch the night bus. I ducked through clothing stalls, skirted by an old-timer stir-frying grasshoppers, caught the waspish fumes of garlic and chilli in soy. A hand touched the wad strapped around my waist. I swung my arm back, turned to see a Thai girl tumble into a rack of tie dye sarongs. 'Shit. *Pom Khor Thod.*' I pulled her from her colourful nest, lifted the knocked clothes rail, and attempted to rearrange the sarongs. The stall owner, an ancient toothless woman wearing an Iron Maiden T-shirt, ushered me away. I'd caused enough damage. The girl brushed herself down, took my hand and smiled. '*Sawadee Ka*. We go for drink, yes?' '*Mai. Khop khun khap.* I must meet my friend.' Her smile inverted to a cartoon frown. 'Maybe later?' she says. 'Chai. Later.' I break free of her grip, catch her glance at my midriff as I turn away.

Lucky Beer hadn't changed. Same DJ banging out tunes, sweaty *farangs* throwing back cocktails, locals distributing food and drink. The room was building a head of steam. In another hour, all would spill dancing onto the street. I planned to be gone by then. I climbed the steps to the upper level in search of a seat and spotted the bald dome of Uku in a darkened corner. He tipped his bottle of Chang in my direction, as if expecting me. I sat beside him, facing the room. '*Sawadee Kap, migo.*' 'Hey, Uku.' I asked a passing waiter for two Chang, looked up to the TV screen facing our corner. The twin towers were still collapsing. 'Sorry bout the shite in New York.' 'We had it coming, *migo*. We had it coming this long while.' The waiter placed two beers on paper napkins, along with a small bowl of nuts. 'Rosie's dead.' 'No way.' 'Fraid so, *migo*. Freak accident.' 'Hit her head doing back flips?' 'How the fuck do you know that?' 'An accident waiting to happen. When did she...' 'Bout eighteen months ago. She'd been living with me, rented my spare room since that morning in The Pit. Quite the character.' 'She was that.' 'Sorry, *migo*. Should have let you know.' 'Makes no odds. Not like I could have come over for the funeral or anything.' 'She loved you, *migo*. "Three-Piece is kind," she used to say. "Three-Piece is one kind muthafucka. He just won't admit it." Reckon she expected you to walk into The Pit some morning and offer her a lift back to New York.' 'Would she have gone back?' 'No. She just wanted to tell you to go fuck yourself.' We laughed, clinked our bottles. 'To Rosie.'

We observed the room for a few moments, the carefree vibe of the tourists in stark contrast to the twin towers collapsing again and again on multiple screens. 'We gave her quite the farewell.' 'Yeah?' 'Yeah. She was right popular downtown, despite being contrary as a 'gator with toothache. Found close to fifteen thousand dollars in her room. Weren't nobody to send it to. She never spoke of family, never received no post. Hell. I didn't even know her last name.' 'It was a Polish name,' I said. 'Kowalski or something... What'd you do with the cash?' 'Threw a wild three-day party at The Pit, with Rosie's casket on a pool table, then buried her in Greenwood Cemetery.' 'Greenwood?' 'The most upmarket cemetery in Florida. Tree-lined avenues, landscaped gardens, where all the rich folk bury their kin. You'd wanna see the looks on their faces when two-hundred Banditos thundered through the manicured grounds towing Rosie's casket. Them folks didn't know what the fuck was going on.' I laughed at the vision of Rosie's final journey, creating one last crazy scene on her way out. 'I had her headstone erected a couple of months back.' 'Yeah? What's the inscription?' 'Here lies Rosie. Super Sharp Shooter.' 'She'd love that.' 'I reckon so, *migo*. I reckon so.' Uku slapped my shoulder and walked towards the toilets. I ordered another couple of beers, watched the room slide towards debauchery. A pang of loneliness shot through me. I may have never seen Rosie again, but it was comforting to know she was out in the world somewhere, shooting pool in a sleazy bar, cracking skulls with her shillelagh, willing to go wherever the night might lead.

Uku returned as the waiter placed our beers on the table. 'Makara said you'd been in touch.' 'Makara's one straight up *hombre*.' 'He's a sound head, alright. You loaded up?' 'Loaded up with nowhere to go.' He points his bottle at the TV screen. 'I switched to the gel. Cheaper, easier to transport. Then this shit goes down.' He takes a swig, laughs. 'Is what it is, *migo*. I'll treat it as an opportunity for an extended vacation. Your snow-white complexion tells me you're just off the plane.' 'Arrived a few hours ago. Mate's banged up in Surat Thani.' 'You here to pay off the cops?' 'Yeah. Twenty grand and he cuts them in on the deal.' 'They know you're here?' 'Don't think so. Three-Piece ain't the name on my passport.' 'Anybody else know?' 'A girl outside. Patted me down from behind.' 'That's a potential complication, *migo*. You travelling tonight?' 'Going to grab the night bus.' 'You're going to walk into crooked cops carrying twenty grand?' 'Don't have much choice.' 'Sounds like you're in need of a wing man.' 'Since you're not busy...' 'You got it, *migo*. I'm in the mood for a moonlit drive.' 'Hope you're not getting any romantic notions.' 'Maybe I am, *migo*. The tropics do strange things to a man.' 'I'll take my chances.'

We threw back our beers, chased them with a couple of Red Bulls and left through the back door. Uku led the way through a succession of narrow streets, passing the street food market before hanging a left onto Soi Kraisi. A couple of hundred metres up the street, a Thai boy sat on a chopped Harley loaded with large pannier bags and a bedroll. Uku high fived the boy, handed him fifty baht, took a key from his pocket and started up the bike. Its feral roar drew all attention to us. Groups of youngsters pointed and gathered round. Uku looked to me. 'Mount up, *migo*.' I climbed onto the pillion seat and we took off, thundering through narrow streets, weaving through tuk-tuks, cars, bicycles, trucks, pedestrians, and scooters. Carcinogenic humidity gave way to a fragrant breeze as we left the chaos of Bangkok behind and headed south on the highway.

We drove through the night, the low guttural growl of the chopper our soundtrack, stopping to refuel, knock back Red Bull, and share spliffs. As we approached Surat Thani, flamingo-pink bands spread across the sky by the rising sun distracted from my sore backside. Macaques watched us pass from undergrowth at the edge of the treeline. The resigned expression on their wizened faces seemed ominous. I inhaled deep of the salt air, watched a fish eagle thread thermals overhead, fingered the cash strapped to my waist. The police station was on Namueang Road, near the harbour, a white rectangular two-story with a line of fluttering flags and a large forecourt. We drove by, pulled over by the river a couple of streets away, spent twenty minutes or so stretching by a bench. None of the passers-by paid us any mind. Just another couple of *farangs* in town to catch a ferry to Samui. I sat on the bench, ripped the wads from my waistband and placed them in a khaki knapsack Uku threw at my feet. I left my small rucksack beside it. 'I'll text once I know it's safe.' 'I'll be here, *migo*.'

The police station stank of carbolic acid. I pulled the slip of paper which Olivia had given me from my wallet and approached a battle-scarred bamboo counter, behind which sat an equally battle-scarred officer. He watched me approach, expressionless, oblivious to the choking fumes. 'I'm looking for Sergeant Huang.' He stared. My eyes strayed to the stripes on the short sleeves of his pressed shirt. I yanked my T-shirt up over my nose for fear of passing out. 'Snakes,' he said, and leaned back in his chair, as if that solitary noun explained everything. 'Sergeant Huang?' 'You Ireland man?' 'Irish. Yes. I'm here to see my friend.' A tailless gecko dropped from the ceiling, landed on the counter, scurried off, flopped onto the floor, froze. I watched its skin turn the off-white hue of the tiles. 'You Ireland?' 'Yes.' He turned his head and barked an instruction in Thai. Another officer emerged from a door to the rear of the room. The sergeant stood, grabbed a wooden truncheon. His colleague replaced him at the counter. 'Come with me.'

I followed the sergeant into a tiny room to one side of the reception area, bare aside from three rickety chairs and a Formica-topped desk. He closed the door, clunked his truncheon onto the desk, and turned to face me. The stench was worse in the tiny space. He watched me pull my T-shirt higher over my nose. 'Snakes,' he said. 'You have money?' 'Yes.' He looked me up and down, obviously expecting me to present him with the money. 'I have the money.' I placed my phone and wallet on the desk by the truncheon, pulled out my pockets. 'But not here. I bring when I see my friend.' He took a few seconds to register what I'd said, walked behind me and patted me down, stood back and glared. A long silence was punctuated by a disjointed rhythm of horns blaring from the street, the chatter of parakeets from outside the barred window. 'Your friend. Snake man.' He seemed to be expecting a response. 'My friend?' 'Yes. Your friend. Snake man.'

I was sleep deprived, had glugged Red Bull and smoked Thai weed for the past ten hours. Was it possible a Surat Thani police sergeant was telling me Hatchet had morphed into a reptilian superhero? Seemingly losing patience with my flawed comprehension, the sergeant marched from the room. He returned half a minute later clutching a dead king cobra. He flung it onto the floor at my feet. It was a prize specimen, about six feet in length with a thick muscular body. 'Your friend.' He bent down, gripped the cobra's tail, swung it around and whacked its head off the wall. 'Your friend. Snake man.' He laughed, which heightened my fear that not only had I no idea of what was going on, there was little chance of me leaving this stinking cesspit alive. The carbolic acid was obviously to dispose of bodies, the cobra a symbol of what had been done to Hatchet. They had killed a serpent. They were about to kill me.

I smiled, bowed slightly, so the sergeant would relax. I was a second away from throwing a straight right to his chin and making a grab for the truncheon when Hatchet's flatulent cackle pulsed from reception. He sauntered into the room, accompanied by a giggling officer. The sergeant poked my ribs. 'Your friend. Snake man.' Hatchet fist bumped me as if we'd just met on a Galway side street. 'Three-Piece. You took your time.' He consulted his bare wrist. 'You travel by boat or what?' The two police officers cracked up. Hatchet had obviously become Mr Popular. He placed a hand on my shoulder. '*Ar thug tú an spondoolies?*' '*Sea. Suas an bóthar.*' Hatchet looked at the sergeant. 'My friend. He has the money. He gets, yes?' The sergeant nodded. Hatchet pointed at the door. 'Go get the dosh. It's cool.'

I left the station and walked to where Uku lay stretched upon the bench, khaki knapsack beneath his bald head. 'You cool, *migo?*' 'Think so. Weird as fuck in there.' 'Suppose you'll be wanting my pillow.' 'I'll be back with it shortly. I hope.' 'Yeah, well I know where to find you if you ain't.' I returned to the station. The officer at the counter didn't even look up, so I crossed reception and entered the small room. Hatchet and the two officers were sat around the desk shooting the breeze. Hatchet rose from his seat as I entered and took the knapsack from my hand. He unzipped it, peered inside, placed the wads on the desk. 'Now if you gentlemen would be kind enough to give me a receipt, I'll be on my way.' A moment of silence before the three exploded into laughter. The sergeant caught my eye, pointed at Hatchet. 'Your friend. Snake man.' I laughed, anxious to maintain the positive vibe in the room. Hatchet shook hands with the officers. 'C'mon,' he said, and threw the knapsack to me. The sergeant stood. 'Wait.' He picked up the cobra and handed it to Hatchet. 'For you, yes.' '*Kap Khun Kap,*' said Hatchet and accepted the gift.

We walked towards the river, me with the khaki knapsack over my shoulder, Hatchet with the dead king cobra slung around his neck. 'What's with the "snake man" shite?' 'I killed the cobra. Came into my cell, night before last.' 'How'd you kill it?' 'Charmed it.' 'Charmed it?' 'Yep. Got it nice and relaxed, like, then grabbed it by the throat and smashed its head off the wall. The Thais are scared shitless of cobras. The sergeant arrived in with breakfast yesterday, I had the cobra draped over the bars. Thought I was a mighty man altogether. Sorry I didn't hide the fucking thing; they dosed the whole place with carbolic acid, nearly suffocated me with the fumes.' 'When did you add snake charmer to your CV?' 'I've had to charm a lot of snakes this past week. The cobra was the easiest of them.'

We heard the throb of Uku's chopper before we reached the river. He had a local boy sitting on the seat, twisting the throttle. The boy looked about eight, obviously buzzed by the experience of revving a Harley. He was even more excited to see the king cobra around Hatchet's neck. He pointed, leapt off the bike. '*Naja. Naja.*' 'Hatchet, Uku.' 'Hey, Uku.' 'Pleased to make your acquaintance, *migo*. That's quite the necklace.' Hatchet gripped Uku's outstretched hand, adopted a Thai accent. 'They're doing "very special price" down at the station.' Hatchet squinted at Uku. 'I've seen you before.' 'Not in your dreams, I hope.' 'Orlando,' I said. 'Uku dropped me back to the motel. On the Harley.' 'I have you now. How's Rosie?' 'Rosie's dead, *migo*.' 'Sorry to hear that. Back-flips?' Uku looked at me. 'You guys never think to advise Rosie against that particular endeavour?' 'Rosie wasn't one for heeding advice,' I said. '*Naja. Naja.*' Hatchet took the snake from around his neck and held it out to the boy. 'You want?' The boy looked at Hatchet, down at the snake, back up at Hatchet. The morning had shaped to be the most eventful of his life thus far. He eased his two hands forward. Hatchet draped the cobra over skinny, trembling arms, wound the tail around his wrists. The boy smiled, then ran across the narrow road and ducked down a side street. Hatchet laughed at the sight of him straining under the weight of the snake. 'Off to tell his mates he killed a cobra. He'll be known as Snake Boy.' I wanted to call after the boy, advise him to stop, warn him how difficult it is to lose a nickname once it sticks.

Uku scanned the street before turning to Hatchet. 'You clear, *migo*?' 'I'm clear. Better off than before. They'll handle the shipping from here on. Well worth cutting them in.' 'Sweet deal.' 'They'll fuck me eventually, but it'll do for now.' Hatchet grabbed me in a head lock. 'Thanks for coming down, you fucker.' He released me and punched me in the ribs, his favoured expression of gratitude. 'What now?' I asked. 'My gear's over in Hat Salat. May as well head there and chill for a few days before heading back. We can book a flight from Samui.' 'What about you, Uku? There's a hammock on Koh Phangan with your name on it.' 'That sounds mighty tempting, *migos*, but I was heading north when Three-Piece showed up in need of a travelling companion. Think I might get myself back in that direction.' 'Here.' Hatchet roots around in the pockets of his sleeveless jacket and pulls out a business card. 'This is the best hostel in Chang Rai. Ask for Ah Nong, tell her you're a mate of Hatchet. She'll look after you. Has a great suss on the Lahu tribe if you fancy heading into the hills for an opium dream. They'll lock up the bike while you're gone.' 'That sounds mighty fine. I'll check it out.' Uku pockets the card, goes to shake my hand. 'A pleasure crossing paths again, Three-Piece.' I pulled him into a hug. 'You should come to Galway for a visit. We'll show you a good time.' He broke the embrace, mounted the chopper, started up. 'That's what I'm afraid of.' He clunked into first. 'Catch you down the road, *migos*.' We watched Uku speed off towards the highway. 'Where'd you bump into him?' 'Lucky Beer.' 'He's the real deal, that lad.' Hatchet poked me. 'Give me your phone. Better ring Livi and tell her we'll be home in a few days.

Hatchet conked in the passenger seat within fifteen minutes of leaving Dublin airport. The peace was a soothing balm. The mad bastard hadn't shut up since we left Samui. He scored yaba in Hat Rin just before we caught the ferry and couldn't resist dropping 'so we can have a good chat on the way home, like.' When we transferred in Bangkok, I gave in and dropped myself, if only to keep my ears up to speed. I was on the verge of jitters when we landed, so augmented my dose to get me through the drive to Galway. The radio spouted nothing but post 9/11 tripe. I knocked it off and drove in silence, the ghosts of road trips past intruding on my mangled thoughts. We'd just passed Athlone when I saw Rosie back-flipping down the dual carriageway ahead of the car, shillelagh tucked tight beneath her right arm. I followed her onto the exit for Ballinasloe, through three roundabouts, took a left, a right, pulled up in front of white wrought iron gates set into a limestone arch. Through the gates, Rosie backflipped around a familiar courtyard, into the panoptic arms of the sprawling limestone building, its white front door stark beneath an imposing clock tower. I watched her swing her shillelagh as she back-flipped along the front facade, smashing small square panes set in large Georgian windows, back and forth, back and forth, until all the panes were broken. She stopped at the front door, raised her shillelagh, turned towards me, and smiled.

'Three-Piece! Three-Piece!' Hatchet shouting beside me. 'What?' 'You're asleep, you fucker.' 'No, I'm not.' 'You were snoring, for fuck's sake. What are we doing here? They built the bypass for good reason, you know.' I read the plaque set into the left pillar.

BORD SLÁINTE AN IARTHAIR – OSPIDÉAL NAOMH BRÍD. WESTERN HEALTH BOARD – ST BRIGID'S HOSPITAL.

'Three-Piece! You alright?' 'They took psychiatric out of the name.' 'It was never in the name, not in our time.' 'You sure?' 'It's been St Brigid's Hospital since the fifties. Fuck this shithole. It's in the past.' The two of us sat in silence, looking through the gates at the abandoned building, its windows intact, its clocktower silhouetted against a shepherd's sky the hue of a fresh scab. Hatchet touched my elbow. 'We've come a long way.' 'We're four feet from the front gate.' I reversed onto the road, drove through the roundabouts towards the bypass. Hatchet glanced at me as I shifted through the gears and got up to speed. 'You know what I mean,' he said. 'Yeah. I know what you mean.'

DIGITAL OISÍN

Ferdia would say, *Go to street view, so we can see*
how things are going back home. Pity we can't do a Star Trek
and rematerialise for dinner. I drop in, and it's all queasy
time travel, driving by finger click where we used to thumb it.
The road between Ballyferriter and Dunquin, shockingly small
after Atlantic Avenue-Pacific Street, the skyscrapers of Brooklyn.
Is that a Corsa coming? The kind of take-it-or-leave-it summer car
I imagine the landlady leaves for John at Teeravane
when they rent the house for August, Madrid's compulsory month off.
The only thing is — he can't drive. He'll spend it looking:
rain in sunlight on fuchsia, sparrows under tears of God, foreign flowers
growing out of stone, invasive and beautiful. Valentia stone
wall patterning — looks loose, cunning assemblage. He'll spend it there,
the last rucked baize of land before the saw teeth — the Atlantic's boom
far and dreamy. The Opel comes, but I go right through; I'm
insubstantial. Bikes outside the Siopa Cat Dubh: Gaeltacht girls
stopping for 99s. But the riders' faces are turned from me —
towards the sea — as I search for Dún an Óir,
Fort del Oro. What were those Spanish sailors' names?
Click, click... The photos wall-papering this sky let in
not a sliver of voidness. It's always summer in street view, winter omitted
when the hedgerows scrape like witch fingers; always summer,
tourist season mild back West, where the peninsula
ends in shark fins, both cliff and mountain. Is that Dónall chatting to Ferg,
outside Kanes, increasingly, Tig Uí Chatháin's less and less?
When I'm close enough to open the door, they disappear. *Hello,*
No Face. One last address. I know my parents' house by the trees.
In the river village, turn right at Guerin's, under the sign of the kingfisher.
On Main Street, people are chatting, their faces blanked as if sliced.
I turn in, before the Elvers. This new magic fails at the gate:
I can't cross the cattle grid.

DAVID MCLOGHLIN

HARBOURSONG, DUBLIN

I home to the water, a port to run
to, porcupine punker spikes of tallship
masts clearing the horizon just for fun
like highjumpers, so you can see them rip

the skyline, facing out, for miles, and when
you can't, you smell it. The harbour. Land me
in a church square, I'll sniff it out, fen-
sweet: the swollen kelp, tide-bloated; and sea-

ochre iron, twisting tenor notes from
the salt wind, parting song, a call. I come.

EVA H.D.

IDIR DÁ ABHAINN

(I) THE BURN DALE — AN DAOIL

Os mo chomhair amach ón teach seo,
i measc na gcnocán, sníonn
an abhainn a bhfuil ainm
Ultaise agus Gaeilge
uirthi,
mar uaim in éadach
an Lagáin.

Thrasnaínn
an abhainn sin achan lá
le freastal ar
The Royal and Prior
Comprehensive School,
scoil a bhunaigh an Rí Séamus I
sa bhliain 1608
chun páistí na bplandóirí
a oiliúint.

Agus is ansin
aisteach go leor,
a d'fhoghlaim mé an Ghaeilge,
ceithre chéad bliain ar aghaidh -

gléasta i ngorm an rí,
le suaitheantas eirmín
ar mo bhrollach -

thugainn
craobhóga na bhfocal
i mo ghlaic

ar ais abhaile
thar uiscí na Daoile.

(II) AN FHINN

Agus ar chúl an tí, sníonn an Fhinn:
abhainn a lean mo shin-sin-seanmháthair,
bean de shliocht na Meanman,
soir ó Ghleann na Finne
go margadh na saoire sa tSráth Bán
le tréimhse a chaitheamh ar an Lagán:
áit ar phós sí,
áit ar labhair sí Béarla amháin
lena clann.

Anois, breis is céad bliain
ina diaidh,
leanann a dubhó
sruth na Finne aniar arís:

agus tá greim agam
ar shnáithe na habhann
i gcathair ghríobháin seo
na staire.

LAOIGHSEACH NÍ CHOISTEALBHA

TURNING PAGES

AOIFE BHREATNACH

My parents' bookcase stood in the kitchen, facing a changing constellation of couches, chairs, and tables. Its contents never changed. New books in bright covers accumulated in other rooms but the creased volumes in the glass-fronted bookcase were static, a relic of their life before children. I often stood before it, my reflection overlaid on the serried ranks of books, rotating the loose handles absently. I hunted for diversion among the yellowing paperbacks, turning them in my hands, wondering if any volume could satisfy that moment's inchoate desires. Knitting and reading, Mum sat on the couch behind me, a watery reflection in the glass. Among William Somerset Maugham and Aleksandr Solzhenitsyn, I found inscriptions from my parent's past: Mum's maiden name, Dad's diminutive 'Óg' or 'Junior'. Neither of these people existed for me but their shadows haunted the bookcase.

Her books come vividly to mind now, because she is dead, and her bookcase is going overseas, where grandchildren she never met will turn a tiny ornamental key in the fragile lock, listening to brass bolts slide back and forth. Mum died in March 2020, seven days after the start of the first Irish lockdown of the pandemic. I had begun a new research project, reading banned books as if I were a filth-hunting censor. Thousands of books were illegal to buy in Ireland between the 1930s and the 1990s—I read Jack Kerouac, then Jackie Collins, bouncing between genres and styles. I grimly cling to this frivolous task when, amidst the hush of lockdown, Mum dies in her own bed. The morning of the funeral I wake up with a temperature. With my siblings stranded abroad, none of her children are there to bury her.

Rage and grief flood, almost drown me. I hold on tight to my books and read on, waiting it out. Reading and being angry were two things my mother did exceptionally well. Her rage could swallow the house whole, it poured from the kitchen into the hallway and flowed up the stairs. Dreadful silence crackled with whiplash fury. There was no talking to her, leaving the room was our strategy. When a clever, controlled woman goes rogue, you hide upstairs. I know those memories are unfair but years of a lingering lung disease— idiopathic pulmonary fibrosis—erased all pleasant memories. Her joy is impossible to remember because she hadn't laughed for ages. Laughter needs breath that she could not spare as her lung capacity shrank. Her sharp intellect faded as she sickened; my questions about growing up in censorship Ireland—she was born in 1945—received scanty answers.

After she dies, I lose myself in these questions. I discover I was raised in the shadow of a remarkably severe censorship regime that began to crumble before I was born in the mid 1970s. Mum grew up a passionate reader when the Censorship of Publications Board placed stringent restrictions on reading, when her reading life was bounded by prohibition orders. I begin to wonder if John McGahern wasn't exaggerating when he said Irish censorship was 'inhuman ... fascistic in the real sense of the word'. It was a heavy judgement from an author who endured public and professional disgrace for writing *The Dark* (1965) a 'dirty' banned book. Yet he was always anxious to preserve his artistic integrity; he refused to blame the censors for a writing drought that followed his involuntary exile from Ireland. It was ten years before he published another novel. If censorship sometimes means words are not written, or are written in different places, what about words not read? I am afraid that my childhood of gluttonous, obsessive reading was formed by inscrutable, remorseless censors.

Extract from the *Register of Prohibited Publications*
Name of Book: Married Love
Editions: All
Name of Author: Marie Stopes
Name of Publisher: G.P. Putnam
Date of Prohibition Order: 9th May, 1930

When I find Stopes on the first edition of the blacklist, I hunt my sagging bookshelves for a copy of *Married Love*. It is a bookish souvenir of a year in Oxford, a year lived in a country where abortions and the morning-after-pill were unremarkable. I find the slim volume but it feels more substantial now that I know it was forbidden to sell it in Ireland until 1979. Mum was pregnant for the fourth and final time that year, when it became legal to publish about contraception. From the first edition of the blacklist, the censors' intentions were clear: they proscribed just three novels but ten sex-education works. In the realm of human biology, authors with MD after their name were not accorded more respect than writers masquerading as sexperts. The ground-breaking Kinsey Reports that described sexual practices in 1950s America were later added to the blacklist alongside early sexologists like Havelock Ellis. Books that advocated natural birth control methods congenial to Roman Catholics were prohibited with the same vigour as those mentioning 'powders lethal to the spermatozoa'. All manner of books about sex were forbidden: serious philosophical treatises, academic studies, guides to technique, meditations on sex in marriage, works on sexual dysfunction. The state labelled anything to do with bodies obscene, meaning photographs of nude women were blacklisted alongside *What Shall I Tell My Child?* by London's Central Council for Health Education in 1944. Literary censorship was effectively abandoned in 1967 but the censors still banned informative publications on sex. *Sex Facts For Teenagers* was outlawed in 1974, *How To Make Love To A Woman* in 1987 and *The G-Spot: In Words And Pictures* in 1992. Silence and secrecy was government policy.

My education ignored the 'facts of life' until Miss Lyons' science class. Staring at my book, at the familiar diagram of the uterus, I could not lift my eyes from the page. Perched on a high stool in the science lab, I tried to shuffle my short grey skirt down to cover my snagged tights. There was barely a sound as Miss Lyons said penis and then vagina over and over again. A few months into our first year in a new school, the class was awkward and confused, aching with embarrassment, bursting with silence. We listened meekly as she powered through the chapter, throwing scary words at us as if it didn't matter. When we clattered out of the class, nobody joked or imitated her nasal voice saying 'testicles'. Wordlessly, we agreed not to talk about it.

Two years later, formal sex-education lessons were pioneered in my newly founded, mixed, multi-denominational secondary school. For this class we were segregated by gender, to sit before a slide show about sperm and eggs, where they came from and how they met. It was the basic mechanics of sex from science class, but the images were of real sperm seen through a microscope, not line drawings. None of this information was new. It was a fuzzy, grainy reiteration of our first-year science class except for the atmosphere. A class that began edgy and excited became bored then contemptuous: yet another lesson on how pregnancy happened but nothing about how to stop it. We knew condoms existed and we were insulted nobody thought we knew. The teacher refused to take questions and the lesson ended with our ignorance intact. This farce was rowdily condemned in the corridors, proof of our teachers' manifest failure to do their job. We were contemptuous of teachers who were too scared to tell us the truth.

Girls relied on each other to share precious knowledge about bodies in a society where sex was almost invisible. My friend Ann, born at the end of the Second World War, told me how she learned 'the facts of life'. A true-blue Dubliner, Ann often walked into town with her mother, buying a few groceries as they enjoyed the city's evening bustle. They occasionally stopped at the Legion of Mary book stall, a barrow on wheels manned by volunteers selling religious literature with titles like *Mary Shall Reign* and *Edel Quinn: A Heroine Of The Apostolate*. To support the women standing for hours in the city streets, her mother occasionally bought a booklet. One evening, Ann noticed the purchased pamphlet was quickly slipped in her mother's coat pocket. Knowing better than to ask, she resolved to hunt for it at home. The next day, she held a little book perforated into two halves in her hands: one side covered facts of life for girls, the other for boys. She read both sides, paying particular attention to the side about boys' bodies. Unable to keep the secret to herself, she gave the book to a friend, who loaned it her friend, who passed it onto her sister who gave it to a neighbour. In a world where panicked mammies called the doctor when their daughters began to menstruate, secret knowledge rippled below the surface of girlhood. Groups of girls giggling on front steps and sauntering through town could subvert all the plans of men in suits and soutanes. Ann tracked the pamphlet's progress through the neighbourhood, until it vanished, probably confiscated by an outraged mother. When her own periods started, Ann's mother gave her the girl's half of the perforated booklet, saying nothing about the first, missing copy. Her girlfriends never forgot their lessons, calling after each other as they promenaded with their fellas, 'See ya. Be good and if not, buy a pram.'

```
Extract from the Register of Prohibited Publications
Name of Book: Country Girls, The
Editions: All
Name of Author: Edna O'Brien
Name of Publisher: Hutchinson & Co. Ltd., London
Date of Prohibition Order: 21st June, 1960
```

Meeting Caithleen, the heroine of the infamously 'indecent' *The Country Girls* (1960) for the first time, I wonder did O'Brien deliberately name her for Cathleen Ní Houlihan, the personification of Mother Ireland? O'Brien's Caithleen was not the weary old woman of literary tradition but a bookish, romantic young girl searching for independence. Her best friend and occasional enemy was Baba, a pet form of Bridget. During the 1930s, the cult of St Bridget was revived to inspire girls to dress modestly in the true tradition of Irish femininity. But O'Brien's Baba/Bridget is brassy, getting a malicious thrill from flaunting her prettiness and material possessions before poor, plain Caithleen. I am thrilled at the audacity of naming a brazen hussy after a saint associated with modest dress and deportment.

Dreamy Caithleen appears to be a stereotypical 'country girl' when she moves to Dublin: working in a shop, boarding with a landlady, and sharing a room strewn with underwear and shoes with her best friend Baba. Contemporary readers are often disappointed that the girls' adventures in the city are not as salacious as the book's reputation. Now, it reads as more charming than corrupting. Reading is inextricably bound up with Caithleen's relationships with men: Baba instructs her not to ask fellas if they've read Joyce's *Dubliners*, telling her 'they're not interested'. Even as a child, literature and love affairs were intertwined for Caithleen, who fixated on a man called De Maurier, a surname that recalls the author of *Rebecca*. When Caithleen first met Eugene Gailliard – a married, non-Catholic, English man as old as her father – she was 'the literary fat girl'. As they conversed alone over coffee, Eugene's erotically-charged opening question was 'Tell me, what do you read?' She blurted out Joyce, Chekhov, and Stephens before suddenly stopping, fearful of showing off. A test was passed: he decided to lend her some books. Later this promise was fulfilled when he loaned her *The Body and Mature Behaviour*, subtitle: *A Study of Anxiety, Sex, Gravitation and Learning*. An unusual choice for a lover, but Eugene was trying to help Caithleen overcome her physical revulsion of sex. She was deliriously happy in his arms until his caresses turned her body rigid with fear. Her flesh shivered and stiffened, rejecting the man in spite of her yearning. She thought 'If only people just kissed, if all love stopped at that', she dreaded the approach of bedtime and fears sex between them as a horrible inevitability. Poor Caithleen is not tortured by religious guilt but she is wordlessly, physically revolted by the act of love. Talk of sexuality or reproduction had always distressed her: when Baba told her about breastfeeding, the bile rose in her throat. Her blindness was so complete, her frame of reference for physical life so inadequate that her body shuns her lover even as she sleeps. This frigidity tortures Caithleen who was profoundly ashamed at her failure to please a man she adored. When sex finally happened, she repeated to herself 'I am not afraid, I am not afraid'.

In spite of her literary ambitions, Caithleen's reading choices have not prepared her for physical love. The Censorship, as the Board was often called, which controlled her reading, tolerated a quick chaste kiss but other depictions of, or references to, heterosexual love were banned. Her Joycean interests were confined to *Dubliners* because *Ulysses* was carefully suppressed. Caithleen's stunted imagination and the fear deep within her body was the result of carefully, deliberately cultivated ignorance. Both fiction and non-fiction were brutally censored for sexual content and reproductive information. Baba, who never reads, is quick and street-wise. Free from the censors' imaginative universe, she experiences her world and her body without reference to permitted reading material. Even as a child, Baba knew the power of forbidden filth, inscribing 'dirty' words on Caithleen's arm with an indelible pen. Their expulsion from convent boarding school – devised by Baba – is precipitated by a lewd sentence about a nun and a priest's 'thing' on a picture card of the Holy Mary. Caithleen admired and feared her best friend's brassy confidence, thinking 'There are no innocent girls ... They're all scarlet girls like Baba, with guile in their eyes'. Although Baba was a self-centred sometimes cruel girl, she was also a brisk no-nonsense woman of the flesh who said unthinkable words like 'preggo'. She knew Caithleen was fettered by her imagination; her repeated refrain 'You're a right-looking eejit' exhorts her friend to be less dreamy, to pay attention to her place in the world in order to manipulate it.

Extract from the *Register of Prohibited Publications*
Name of Book: Complete Guide to Sex, The
Editions: All
Name of Author: Not recorded
Name of Publisher: Not recorded
Date of Prohibition Order: 27th July, 1990

I was a pure eejit because I didn't even know where the solitary scuffed-looking condom in my boyfriend's wallet came from. Of course I knew it wasn't easy to procure them. You had to ask in the chemist shop, walking straight up to the white-coated professional behind the counter to ask for a box of johnnies. The idea of telling a shop full of strangers you were having sex was unimaginable. There was no condom in my purse because I knew I could not have sex. Sex meant pregnancy, that looming, dark horror that haunted us all. School-girl pregnancy was the greatest catastrophe; a girl who got pregnant in school was a failure who spoiled everything, who threw away her chances. I fervently believed this even though girls in my school regularly got pregnant and walked the crowded corridors as usual, bearing their bellies through our sharp elbows and slung schoolbags. After the birth, they returned to school in the same sloppy jumpers and micro minis as before while granny minded the baby. Life after teenage pregnancy didn't look that different to before but it still appalled me.

In a country where abortion was illegal, pregnancy always meant birth. For adults, information about services abroad was passed through clandestine networks of graffiti, leaflets and voluntary phone lines but our toilet wall was more 'Gemma HEART Sully' than illegal information highway. There wasn't even a sanitary products dispenser next to the sinks blocked with shiny-paper loo roll. I dimly understood 'the boat to England' meant more than a ferry journey but as a schoolgirl in a nasty acrylic jumper I could not translate that phrase into 'travelling to England for an abortion because I cannot get one here'. Irrevocable pregnancy-disaster was never far away when I fooled around on the bottle-strewn edges of sports fields, ankle deep in soft pine needles and crisp packets. We breathlessly lifted shirts and opened jeans, furtive reaching for skin. I took risks, knowing seminal fluid laced with sperm leaked out but desire for a silky-hard cock-head pushed fear aside. Lust barrelled past danger, hot mouthed and horny. Afterwards, waiting for monthly cramps was a torment of anxiety and fear.

Crouched over a homework assignment, the nagging worry would transform into panic and terror so enveloping that my hand would stop writing. Wasn't my period due? Could it be late? Shit, shit, shit. I beat my belly hard, punching it repeatedly, determined to root out tenacious embryos. Again and again, my tight fists strike hard, until I cannot do it anymore. Nothing happens. There are no cramping pains but I convince myself the dull ache lies in my womb. Until my period starts, womb-beating is a ritual performed most mornings and evenings. When cramps finally happen, the dread evaporates and I forget all my terror to begin afresh. Every month I seek pleasure in another body and each month I carry a suffocating fear of pregnancy. Pregnancy, I believe, will be irreversible and terminal. Worse than pregnancy is knowing I would stand in front of my mother and say 'I'm pregnant': the heaviest, most disgraceful words imaginable. When beating my belly, I imagine telling her, standing in the kitchen and delivering the worst news ever. During this just-in-case mental preparation, I never say the words but I know her anger and disappointment would dwarf my paltry guilt. Her capacity for rage over small things was immense, I shrink before the image of her justifiable fury. But I was lucky, I was never caught out. I got away with it.

Extract from the *Register of Prohibited Publications*
Name of Book: Little Red Schoolbook, The
Editions: All
Name of Author: Soren Hansen & Japser Jensen
Name of Publisher: Stage 1
Date of Prohibition Order: 24th May, 1972

Our ignorance, fear and confusion was fostered by a long-standing, thoroughly enforced censorship policy. Useful books that would have expanded our knowledge, like *The Little Red Schoolbook (LRSB)*, were banned decades before. The *LRSB* caused a sensation in Europe in the early 1970s when governments decided the youth needed to be shielded from an immoral and corrupting text. The cheeky reference to Mao Tsetung's *Little Red Book* was only partly a joke: this book was a manifesto on children's rights, offering a bald critique of social hierarchies. Like the infamous Communist text, it was a physically small, pocket-sized book. Neatly dressed children could conform to school dress codes while concealing a little book of radical sedition close on their person, in a trouser or uniform blazer pocket. It was small enough to be stuffed into a waistband, then obscured with a regulation-issue jumper when a teacher passed by. The physical form of the *LRSB* revelled in the intimacy between reader and prohibited text, encouraging rebellion against authoritarian school cultures where reading suffocated under mandatory, 'educational' goals.

The *LRSB* text was incendiary: the authors advised children that adults 'can never control you completely', and that reading comics or pornography in boring classes was a rational response to bad teaching. Written in Denmark, where corporal punishment had been abolished, it advised pupils to debate learning strategies with teachers in a collaborative spirit of equality. If this failed, the authors counselled students to find ways to 'escape' by 'mucking about'. In the world of the *LRSB*, children were not intimidated or impressed by baseless adult claims to authority. The translation project of the *LRSB* was intentionally radical, because the text was not directly translated but customised to each nation's school system. Children could read about their own school systems from the perspective of Danish authors who wished to transform pedagogy and cultures of authority. As translations of the *LRSB* spread across Europe, governments and hierarchies sensed its traitorous potential.

In England, social conservatives were horrified by the frank discussions of sex, sexuality, and contraception. Purity crusader Mary Whitehouse was worried the girls who followed the book's suggestions to masturbate would never be satisfied by penis-in-vagina sex. Too many girls pleasuring themselves instead of assuming their reproductive burdens would lead, inevitably, to the end of the world. After Whitehouse helped prosecute the *LRSB* as obscene, the publishers produced an expurgated edition that deleted some references to condoms. This cleaned-up version was imported into Ireland in 1972 by George Solomos, an American poet and film-maker. He distributed a mere 350 copies before it was banned. Solomos' provocative actions drew the government's attention, who directed the full machinery of the state to scrutinise his immigration status. A man from the 'Alien's Office' visited Solomos' offices, questioning the staff about their nationality. The censors wrote to inform him of the prohibition order, which was swiftly followed by a Garda visit although the censors never normally corresponded with publishers. Undeterred by intimidation, Solomos announced he was compiling a *Little Green Schoolbook* that would be specific to Irish circumstances and escape the censors' wrath. He knew that the dangerous heart of this pocket-sized volume was not its sex education chapters but its anti-authoritarian message.

An Irish schoolbook would have asked children to challenge teachers who had the right to beat them with straps, rubber hose pipes, and sticks. Corporal punishment, which was legal until 1987, crystallised the author-itarian, rote-learning culture of Irish schools in the 1970s. Equality was an impossible dream for children caught in a system that did not grant them fundamental human rights. For decades, parents had complained about beatings so severe that children came home bruised and bleed-ing but government rarely intervened to control teachers. This was the violent, cruel society that George Solomos tried to challenge with a little book written in plain English, small enough to fit in a child's coat pocket. Unfortunately, he never published a miniature book of revolutionary ideas because he was deported in August 1972 after the government refused to renew his visa. Solomos was convinced that the decision was 'purely a censorship thing. They don't like what I'm saying'.

Extract from the *Register of Prohibited Publications*
Name of Book: Sex
Editions: All
Name of Author: Madonna
Name of Publisher: Martin Secker & Warburg Ltd.
Date of Prohibition Order: 20th November, 1992

Foreign ideas promoted by foreigners had an offensive quality. In May 1992, two thousand copies of the *Guardian* newspaper were withdrawn from circulation. The importers ripped out the full-page ad for Marie Stopes clinics and shredded it before sending the paper out for sale. A few months later, such newspaper ads were granted constitutional protection: the electorate agreed that pregnant people had a right to information about abortion services available abroad. A week before the polls opened, the Censorship Board banned Madonna's glossy coffee-table volume of explicit photos, *Sex*. Nobody noticed or objected because no one believed the censorship of Madonna had anything in common with abortion information.

Her provocative book was dismissed by the serious male reviewers because they found her distasteful. John Banville wrote 'She is a street-corner kid, the worst girl in class, the one who does unspeakable things with boys behind the bicycle shed and laughs about it afterwards'. Untrustworthy girls who refused shame were not artists. Madonna was the sound track to our girlhood in the 1980s: we felt the challenge in her swagger but we didn't fully comprehend why what she said or did was controversial. We grew into her rebelliousness, adopting her words and gestures as we caught up with her. In our final year 'Debs Ball' in secondary school, we dressed up in shiny satin and wore our hair big, crackly with hair spray. The hotel ballroom was crowded with teenagers in adult clothing, holding their bodies awkwardly, shuffle-dancing in borrowed shoes. One shining incident distracted us as we idled around our tables, wondering when the pantomime would end. A group of girls took to the small brightly lit stage and grabbed a microphone. They sparkled under the lights, their dresses and eyeshadow throwing light into the dim ballroom. When the words about virginity rang out, the silence in the room deepened. One gyrating girl was heavily pregnant and the others were all teenage, unmarried school-going mothers. Their performance was a brazen fuck you to all of us who pitied them, who believed their pregnancies were a misfortune. Some girls, the worst girls, refused shame, singing their raucous defiance into the silence.

Extract from the *Register of Prohibited Publications*
Name of Book: Abortion: Our Struggle For Control
Editions: All
Name of Author: Various
Name of Publisher: The National Abortion Campaign, 374 Gray's Inn Road, London WC1
Date of Prohibition Order: 30th September, 1983

On college enrolment day we queued in long snakes around the quadrangle which, in a joke typical of our city, was three-sided. By day's end everyone carried a welcome pack from the student's union in a large plastic bag, one for boys and one for girls. For the first time in my life, I'm given free tampons. Peering into the plastic bag to see tampons next to flyers, free pencils, and a campus map was vaguely thrilling. A rumour spread that the boys had condoms in their bag, but that was too incredible to be true. Some girls whinged that it wasn't fair, they didn't even use tampons, what good were these things anyway? Yet again we were 'girls' with 'girls'' bodies. 'Boy' and 'girl' welcome packs felt ridiculous; our bodies were getting in the way again, segregating us on the very first day. I longed to be bodiless, I hoped college would mean my 'girl' status would fade into the background. The tiny school skirt and snagged tights were binned without hesitation but gender never relaxed its grip.

Information about contraception and abortion were no longer illegal but censorship was reflexive, and emotions of disgust evoked by unspeakable, filthy bodies lingered. The spectre of pregnancy, its weight and finality, hung over university as it had in school. Now I knew where to get condoms—thanks to Richard Branson and the Virgin Megastore. I was less sure where to get an abortion other than England. The second constitutional referendum on abortion was held two years before I went to college, when the electorate acknowledged England was essential to reproductive health in Ireland. Astonishingly, the voters refused to reaffirm the right to life; they didn't take the opportunity to rank the lives of foetuses over pregnant people. This small change from the 1987 referendum, where the right to life of the unborn was asserted in the Eighth Amendment, felt momentous. This sliver of possibility, that abortion was no longer unthinkable, was debated endlessly among my group of tea-drinking, argumentative friends. The more tea we drank, the more intimate we became. Only friends who knew each other well could broach a topic as dangerous as abortion. Pro-lifers had a college society, alongside role-players, choristers, and accountants. There was no corresponding pro-choice society.

None of us had been old enough to vote in the 1992 referendum so we debated the moral rights and wrongs of abortion regularly. Is it okay to end a pregnancy? If so, why? What circumstances make this a good choice or a bad choice? Because we were young and optimistic or because we fancied ourselves as debaters, we didn't propose arguments around gritty uncompromising life situations. Always we circled around punishment and risk. Sex was risky and pregnancy was the punishment for sex: the question was, how will you take your punishment, in pregnancy or in abortion? Which shameful thing would you endure: unmarried motherhood or the boat to England? While we obsessed over the consequences of heterosexual sex, gay people in our group were subdued. Debates were focused and insular, bounded by fear. We pushed against the same arguments each time, against the boundaries of our social imagination, trying to see a way out. It was a maze and we were lost without maps or theories. All I knew was that I could not, would not, be pregnant but I was also having sex. Fatalistic now, I didn't beat my stomach each month. We were stuck, trapped in a game of chance playing for life and death stakes. We couldn't see that the game was rigged: the high stakes, not sex or abortion, were the problem. Everyone knew girls couldn't be trusted, their fickle, unpredictable bodies refused to be subdued.

As the pandemic fades, I return to second-hand bookshops–searching for banned books sold when prohibition orders were in force, hoping to track clandestine readerly rebellions. I note imprint dates and think about chronologies, but I find very little evidence of banned books in circulation. Often, more often than I am ready for, I see a familiar cover, a duplicate from my mother's bookcase. Perhaps the original owners were committed de-clutterers, but I suspect these are donations from the dead. Readers born in the 40s are dying, leaving their heirs to carefully pack up cherished Walter Mackens, dusting volumes of W. Somerset Maughan's short stories before selling them. Grief moves through me when I open a book, but I welcome how old paper's dry tang evokes my mother's kitchen. I can hear her metal knitting needles click-clacking. The tips are bright with wear, winking in the sunlight as wool dances through her fingers. As always, she is reading a book, travelling through a world beyond her kitchen and her life with us. If I call her, she will not answer. I hold my breath, tasting an old bookshelf's silence, wondering what words censors withheld from us and mourning the forbidden books we never read together.

BOOK ON THE BYPASS

And what story   was she trying to tell me
lying there   so open wounded
in the middle of the road
                        with her skirts about her head

fluttering
                        at the will of every gust
with not a single car to stop
                to lift her up beyond her print.

And the greedy wind, trying to decide
        which line is most essential to the plot
fights to read them all at once;
        as though the words were not enough.

Print redacted black from rain.
                Pages threatening to leave their spine.
And what did she say so loudly
                        to make her end up there?

At once that paper looked like skin
                and fingertip soft, and so inviting in.
What would I have had to risk
                        by going back?

To lift her up from all of that?
        Chip my nails; my fingers to their bones,
scrape the backs of my hands:
                        leave my skin on the road.

MARTINA DALTON

LAID OUT

who do you want to be

careful how you answer

your mother knew about the illusion of choice / knew no matter what promise the moon made peering out from behind the trees at the bottom of the long garden / in the morning she still woke in the same tired body / throat closed shut / blood seeping through the towel between her legs onto the sheet / the weight of an unspoken life hidden by her careful movements / getting out of bed making breakfast dropping the youngest off at school

you remember the shadow cast by that weight
it carried its own familiar scent
sometimes you go back to that place search it out
spray it on the tender flesh of your wrist
hold it to your nose drink in
its heavy promise

who did she want you to be

careful with the words you place in her mouth

your mother *was* proud of you

LAID OUT

you know that   a matter of fact

but there was envy too

she gifted you a spoken life and you reached out and took it from her /
then came the distance between the unspoken and the spoken / each syl-
lable each cycle of the moon moving you further apart

does the word *betray* apply here

if you placed that word in her mouth
would it belong there
would she choose to utter it

she's sitting in the chair to the left of the fireplace / the weight is settled
in her lap / its scent seeking you out / you take a step back / then another

do you feel torn

in that moment you are neither
spoken or unspoken / you belong nowhere

who do you think they want you to be?

careful   they may not like the answer

there are four children's voices speaking over each other

*the featherweight of a fifth / a blurred memory of a toilet cubicle / the
nurse taking the towel which had been pressed between your legs / her*

voice echoing off the enamel surfaces / registering what your body had
expelled three moon cycles in

> *the fifth voice   unspoken   once was briefly*
> *a purity to the silence between you*
> *it asks nothing of you   wants nothing from you now*
> *it has no scent*
> *you attach no word to your side of the silence*

the other four

yes you are their mother / you give them use of that word / allow them to
speak it freely / it belongs /doesn't belong to you

> the moon you've left peering through the trees
> at the end of the long back garden

your body full throated now

released from all questions

lays
                itself
                                down

ANNE TANNAM

ADHLACADH MO DHEIRFÉAR

Brádán
báistí ag bagairt
cóisir chlabhtaí
ag síneadh romhainn
cochall gorm
i bhfoirm dín

scraitheanna sleabhctha
sínte go leataobh

cnámharlaigh a muintire
á múscailt
ón néal sámh
á fáiltiú
chun suain síoraíochta

cogarnach chiúin
á chogaint
ó bhéal fir
faoi chumhdach
i bhfcistcas róba
ag clupaideach
i bhfeadaíl gaoth shiógach

focail is easparta
nár chualathas
ach a chonaiceas
i mbéal mná

dallta a d'fhéachadar
— na taibhsí úd —
tharam

JULIE BREATHNACH-BANWAIT

HUMAN

The boy shouts at first, amid the rucks of lino,
the peephole cigarette burns, the sunders and scuffs,
then eases me up through loose floorboards
from my under-house entombment, sighing
at my lightness, the yield of these half-melted bones,
the tanned, shut-eyed face. *Are you human?*
he asks. And I would tell him if I could that this
flopped flesh was regal once, answerable
only to the land, before chokehold and overkill —
the price I would pay for failed corn crop,
cattle murrain. That a larder existed below the run
of sphagnum, tormentil, and bog asphodel,
which kept me for centuries, carried the print
of my every wrinkle, gentled the parabola of my lips.
He, not knowing what he sees, props me
in the bottom of a wardrobe, decides against telling
his drunk, muttering parents. At daybreak
he wraps me in a hoodie, binds me on the carrier
of his bike, and off to school through snarls
of traffic, thrash of storm and deluge. His classmates,
some street-led, others street-given, laugh
when he reveals me, then stare in silence
at my suffered shape. Though there's chaff spilling
from a slit in my gut, and my tongue has turned
to mould, they nudge closer in the drab bicycle shed
beside the schoolyard. Their heads jerk
towards the seeps trickling from my mouth
and eyelets, as though these were speaking.
Everything seems delayed or distanced, the bell-call
to lessons lost through wind and rain beyond
the windows, the push of the future ended.
Slowly, as they make free, puzzling the preservation

a bog can bring, I die again, gently this time,
in the hothouse of their attention. And though
I remain what the earth long ago made me — as good
as mud — for a moment I find myself treated
as their oldest friend, lifted into a communal dance,
where they cast light, or try to, on life's joys
and bothers, on how the world picks holes in them.

PATRICK DEELEY

THE POEM

SONYA GILDEA

She was ten. Almost. In two weeks' time. This is late winter, the year starting cold and February-like outside. She has, for no reason she knows, written a poem. Or what might be a poem, she thinks. Though she cannot remember reading one, or seeing one properly. She doesn't read. Not at all. This is something she will come to, later. She'll be sixteen and then seventeen and a friend, a poet who lives in the nearby town, will give her books. First, Hemmingway, then Sartre, De Beauvoir, and others, dense and thick. She'll read them all, back to back, stunned that she had missed this. That it was going on without her knowing. That it hadn't ever been a part of things.

Back to when she was nine, almost ten. She wrote the poem. It was hand written, in pencil, down one side of the page. She didn't have an influence, or a style or form she was trying to make. All she remembers now is that there was a fountain in part of the poem, and some coins. The coins were already there—in the after-wards—underwater and left. The person, (or throwers) gone.

Later she would remember rain on the grass caught, improbably, in low sun. She would remember being stopped by this, at the kitchen window. Alone, the kitchen unheated and cold. The floor of cement, her breath on the air; the leaving house. But—there was the grass, rain-covered in sun. Like it shouldn't be. This is, in its confusion, what she must have wanted to write about, but that would be later. She would be twelve, almost. Everyone else, in some way, gone. She, walking, always late for the school bus. Uniformed, and distracted. It was the light. How low to the ground it was.

But, that was not the poem. It was the one that had a fountain. How though, she thinks now? There were none in the place of the leaving house. The leaving place. Nothing she had ever seen of inconsequence in the farmlands around. All was functional, transactional: a Cork rural grey.

Her mother asked if she would read the poem for them. By now, her family were all in the upstairs bedroom. This room is built into eaves, the ceiling leans down to meet the window. They are all there. Can that be right, she wonders. But yes, it is. She is standing with her back to the curtained window, her copybook in hand, opened to the back page. She is preternaturally shy. This too won't change. Her sisters and brothers are gathered on the bed, her parents sitting on the edge, side by side.

The difficulty is, she doesn't want to read it, not in this way. Though she doesn't know why. That isn't clear to her. Also, not clear is why it is strange. Uncomfortable, dishonest in some way. But these are new feelings. And, these people are her parents, her family. So, she reads from the copybook.

They are quiet, and happy to hear the poem. Encouraging. When she finishes, they applaud.

It is, if she's right, spontaneous applause. Meant. And it startles her. They are being generous. They are, she knows—at least she thinks she knows—surprised also that she might write a poem. It is a strange, isolated thing to do. Though, interesting maybe.

She doesn't like the applause. Not at all. Though she doesn't understand the dislike she has, how quiet it feels. In her skin, her small body. She is warm, and desperate for it to stop. She thinks the applause is disproportionate.

The poem—and this is the only thing she knows for certain—isn't that good.

They are, have always been, an over-the-top lot. A family given to excess, to emotions that run freely, run high. Musicians. Stagemakers. She knows this too. They're not wrong, nor to be blamed.

She tries to hide what must be shame—though she doesn't know that either. But her skin burns. Her hands are damp, sticky.

She is embarrassed, for the poem, and—here is the shame, she thinks—for them.

She'll never say this. Not once. Not to anyone.

HORSE LATITUDES

I once found a shiny sixpence
in a field where friends said to look,
a trick to stop me following — to find
a thing not lost was the first sorrow.

Or was the first sorrow finding trust
faithless in that sylvan girlhood world,
where I wandered unheard
following a faun deeper into silence?

I did discover true friends, rare fellow-shadows
who dowse themselves in the stillest seas —
unfathomable friends schooled in folding
charted time into memory's deepest pocket.

And here I am, with the gift of dark sweets,
a shiny blank notebook and a card full of love
wishes, only to find within a fortnight I am back
in that childhood field, unfollowing — you,

having shadow-banned me from your virtual
world. And as I sail the horse latitudes
scuffing winter leaves on the forest floor,
I write an apology for... offence unknown.

Ask why. But no response is a response full
of tacks, and I, grown accustomed
to the vagaries of indifferent winds
and feckless friends, will horse my boat
on solitary currents to the fastening flame
at the centre of the wood, where my faun awaits.

ELEANOR HOOKER

ULNAR

On preparing for ulnar nerve release surgery

Ulnar is an island in the Hebrides, heavy with sheep,
or a Lake District mere: Ullswater is my parents' favourite.
Windermere is longest, Mam said, but Ullswater is quiet.
Úll is an apple in Irish, the urge to bite a mouthful
from my elbow, its inner crook, where the core is mangled,
to work at the errant pips. Ul, the scooping out of a boat,
this limb for so long my own, now to be marked and slit,
scarred with a tiny grey sail. Ulnar, a messaging system,
swellings in water — whales look shifty, their calves giggle,
but it is all too bone-held and fishy for us to interpret.
Ulnar, an elephant, with checks in every shade of purple.

When they are done, I will feel it again, the nerve
— not a flashing disco, but a channel in a rock, letting
the stream trickle back through, to feed digits and palm,
and they will remember a solidness. I will bend my sore arm
into a V and play guitar, staccato, angst, sunset hot.
I will forget Ulnar, its soft hold, land before hospital,
before gown and stockings, before falling asleep to wake
with new knowledge of my body, before returning to a world
I feel too changed to settle in again, a trapped red moth.
How quickly Ulnar becomes dinosaurs and melted ice,
that big U a meteor crater of all this odd, purple loss.

ELIZABETH GIBSON

THE POET'S COAT

Now that you're dispersed to dust motes
at a bus stop or settled on a window
sill, at rest at last in the evening sun,

I'm left to contemplate your empty coat
shapeless, faded beige, bunched up on a hook.
Silently I search one more time for words,

fragments stuffed inside capacious pockets —
finding nothing I try it on for size,
walk down to the harbour I now call home.

Weary now your coat has shed its pain,
one life lived amongst the fishing boats,
poems wash in on coastal clouds of rain.

MATTHEW GEDEN

CARDINAL

AILEEN HUNT

1.

That first winter in Cincinnati, I bought a red, down jacket. I'd left Ireland mid-June, my suitcase full of the type of light, waterproof clothes perfect for the mild Irish climate. I was fleeing the nest at last, escaping! It never occurred to me that I might be cold.

In fact, I was too hot at first. I struggled with the swampy heat of Cincinnati's summer. The humidity exhausted me. My hair was permanently damp. Whenever I stepped outside, sweat tickled down my forehead. I stopped wearing makeup.

Autumn was a relief. Some days, a slight nip in the air; others warm as a fine summer's day in Ireland. Jeans, t-shirts, sweaters. An old blue rain jacket. My overstuffed suitcase yielded everything I needed. I wasn't worried about winter. How cold could it be?

2.

Among the fourteen trees in our suburban garden: a lime tree, an apple tree, a hundred-year-old red oak. There's a photo of the four kids sitting on one of its thick, steady branches, my husband's unseen hands holding the youngest upright.

The blaze of that garden in Autumn. The sugar maple's twirling descent through yellow, orange, red. The sweetgums dip to purple. The oak tree's scarlet extravagance. My favourite, the Japanese maple. *Bloodgood.* Year-round red deepening to crimson as the yellow school buses plied the road.

One winter, my husband pruned it so severely, I stood in the driveway and cried. I couldn't imagine such a hacked thing ever blossoming again.

'Wait,' my husband said. 'Be patient.'

3.

What I didn't know then was a day can look lovely and still be dangerous. One morning that first year—November or December maybe—we ran
out of coffee. I glanced out of the apartment window at a clear blue sky,
a shining sun. 'I'll drive around to the store,' I said and stepped outside
without my jacket. The cold hit me like a train. My chest caved inwards;
my ribs stung; I couldn't breathe. I thought my heart would freeze, seize
up forever right there in the empty carpark.

4.

It was a puffy, Michelin-man type of thing, but I loved the warmth of it.
When I zipped it up, I felt cocooned from the world, safe from the worst
the weather could throw at me. And I loved the colour. The bright red
never failed to cheer me.

5.

Photos of me wearing my red down jacket:

- In Chicago, hair whipped across my face by the wind from Lake
  Michigan.
- Outside the Children's Museum in Indianapolis, a toddler wrapped
  around my leg.
- On the steps of McMillan Hall, the University of Cincinnati, first
  day of graduate school.
- Standing in our garden after a heavy snowfall, a few days before
  the birth of our first child. A splash of unfastenable red; an
  expanse of white.

6.

The first time I drove in the snow—real, honest-to-goodness, midwestern
snow—I almost crashed the car. The flakes so dense and so heavy, I could
barely see where I was going. I was driving to pick up my husband, but
the road to his office had merged with the parkland surrounding it, and
I'd no idea if I was driving over grass or concrete. I put the car in gear and
hoped for the best.

7.

One year, a neighbour gave us a red sled for the kids. We'd zip them into their snowsuits and pull them up to the top of a hill, then hold our breath as they careered back down without us.

8.

At first, we were confused by the robins, enormous compared to their Irish cousins. Later, we discovered the two birds are not related; their name and red breasts the only reason they seemed familiar. I used to watch them stand on our Cincinnati lawn, yellow beaks tilted to the sky. As if to say, how did we get here?

9.

A male cardinal, splendid in his crested pomp, fluffs his scarlet robe and hops across the snow. A row of tiny crosses in his wake.

10.

We bought a Radio Flyer, the little pull-behind wagon familiar to us from the countless American TV shows and movies we consumed in Ireland. The kids loved it. They'd pile in and beg us to take them to the park, or stuff it full of toys and teddy bears and God knows what. Often, when I was washing dishes at the sink, I'd glimpse it from the corner of my eye, red steel glinting in the sun, white logo swirling across the side.

At some stage, a red bike with training wheels. A red plastic swing seat. A Little Tykes ride-on. Red, of course. A wallpaper with drawings of fat red airplanes and helicopters. Pyjamas with the logo of the Cincinnati Reds baseball team. A red hairband. A red convertible for Barbie.

11.

I'd forgotten. That first summer, the Reds won the World Series, swept the Oakland A's. The two of us, sitting at Riverfront Stadium, the smell of hot dogs and popcorn seeping into our still-white skin. It took ages to figure out the rules of the game; to know when to cheer, when to give up hope.

12.
The three kids were getting easier. They were healthy, doing the things they were supposed to do. We'd always said four. Why not?

13.
1. Your life can change on a dime.
2. The rug can be pulled from under your feet.
3. The wind can be taken from your sails, or
4. The stuffing can be knocked out of you.

14.
Red blood on a white sheet. The image on the screen a weather map; dark snatches of shadow, bright splashes of snow. I couldn't tell if her heart was red, but I could see its pulse. Maybe, it said. Maybe.

Months later, the obstetrician asked if it was okay to pray. The priest hovered outside the delivery room. When they placed her on my chest, I noticed two things. One, she was warm. Two, she had red hair.

15.
Red is the rarest hair colour. The combination of red hair and green eyes even rarer. But rarer still: the number of babies born with an encephalocele, a neural tube defect caused by the failure of the neural tube to fuse properly during gestation.

I was never good at statistics; never really grasped the concept of probability.

16.
Possible outcomes:
Hydrocephalus
Developmental delay
Intellectual disability
Vision impairment
Growth delays
Seizures
Death.

17.
Advice: Hope for the best. Prepare for the worst.

18.
Those robins. Symbol of wisdom in Native America; harbinger of storms in Ireland. In Christian lore, a robin tried to remove the thorns from Jesus' head during the Crucifixion. They say the drops of blood that fell on his breast stained his feathers forever.

19.
Someone wheeled me into Intensive Care—my own body still sore and stitched and swollen—and I looked at her tiny form in its glass incubator; her head bandaged; her mottled limbs a tangle of tubes and wires.

Had they figured out by then that redheads are more sensitive to pain? That the same gene that causes red hair also determines pain response? That redheads require more sedation and more topical anaesthetics?

Those first few days a blur. I don't remember discussing drug choices with her surgeon. I don't remember warnings about side effects. Ototoxicity. What does it matter? I'd still have said yes. Anything to make her better.

20.
A hearing aid dropped on the snow. Red comma on a blank page.

21.
Stitches x-ed like a crown above her forehead. The tube of the shunt visible beneath thin blue skin; curving from the front of her skull, back behind her ear and down the side of her neck towards her stomach. The puckered hollow where the shunt ends. Another angry red line across the back of her neck, just above her hairline. A small u-shaped scar she'll earn when her appendix is removed needlessly in a few years' time. All faded now, except the small white scar at the top of her nose, a reminder of a run-of-the mill bump I treated at home with ice and hugs. A misguided attempt to spare her another trip to the hospital.

22.
Years later, I'll be buying a new duvet and my oldest daughter will suggest

cruelty-free down. I'll realise I've never questioned how down gets from a duckling's breast to the inside of a duvet or a jacket.

Always the littlest ones.

23.

Her initials—unintentionally—the standard abbreviation for Ohio. State bird: the cardinal. State flower: the scarlet carnation. The Buckeye state, cradle of presidents, birthplace of aviation, and—according to Ohio Tourism—the heart of it all.

24.

The drive to protect her scared me; its intensity a revelation. I pressed her to my chest, ready to charge at any threat. More animal than human. Red in tooth and claw.

A brutal regime of therapy and appointments, homework and exercise. Progress and setbacks. The other kids. My husband, rarely.

It took me two years to realise I couldn't do it on my own. I needed my mother's help.

By then, her hair was long enough to cover the scars.

25.

Red orthopaedic boots. Red plastic cutlery, specially adapted. A metal walker glinting on the deck, red plastic handles warm from the sun.

26.

If you ask me, I'll tell you my favourite colour is green, but when we sold the house in Cincinnati, I kept only the red couch. I had it shipped to Dublin and put in our front room. It's long past its best, but I can't bring myself to part with it.

That first winter back, I tried to wear the red jacket. But the weather was never really cold enough. I found myself sweating on the street or in the shops whenever I wore it. It still cheered me up, but I no longer needed its protection.

Eventually, I snagged the pocket on a car door. Bits of stuffing and feathers drifted in my wake, and although I meant to repair the tear, I never did. One day, I was gathering up clothes for the charity shop and spotted the familiar red at the back of the wardrobe. I hauled its weight out and squished it into a black bin bag. Someone else would be glad of it.

27.
The kids are grown now; their American accents long gone. Our eldest daughter was first to fledge. She moved to Austin last year.

Her sister and I visited in September, but first we stopped off in Boston. My husband was flying in later that night, so we had the afternoon to wander around by ourselves. We started at the Harbour and worked our way down to the North End.

When we stopped for pizza, our waiter was wearing a baseball cap and a Red Sox shirt. I was halfway through the first slice when it dawned on me. Two taxis, a transatlantic flight, a long walk through a strange city. No help. No special equipment. I raised my glass and toasted us both.

28.
I'm not saying we escaped unscathed. Nobody's that lucky.

29.
I'm just saying you learn to cobble together a suitable outfit, no matter the weather.

MAL AUX PROP AUX DENTS ISM

Take *all the teeth in China*. Now we tried to calculate this one night over a curry. To come up with a ballpark. So. There're humans, living and dead and their baby teeth and other mammals and theirs. Then there're polyphyodonts, alligators, geckos, caimans but baleen didn't count and we were only talking inland. Immigrant piranha too, a recent addition but plentiful in the way of gnashers... False teeth didn't count, titanium implants a big no no and on the question of decay in a world of root canal, the consensus was *if* it could pass as a tooth to the naked eye, Bob's yer uncle. Then at the snapping crack of poppadom, an urgent, biting question — where are my baby teeth? I mean. Where are they? I could ring home, ask my mother ...*she was on again, asking the daftest of questions, I think she's gone a bit queer, do you think they go a bit funny over there? Teeth this time. Her baby teeth. Christ in Heaven.* In the landfill just outside the town, probably. They called it the dump back then. And they were good teeth, brushed teeth. My poor baby teeth. God I miss them.

JEMMA WALSH

AGUS

To my great-uncle Mort O'Shea (1882-1970) agus to all the ancestors.

I

Tá brón orainn, sorrow is on us, for not learning Irish. 'Paddy and Eileen and all of them,' the family says, 'would run up the Sugarloaf after a goat or a fox to avoid your visits.' If you caught and quizzed them, there might have been a twinkle buried in your schoolmaster's furrow. You knew scarcity, and, much as you loved the language that you were still cutting out of the bogs, you knew why your nieces and nephews were making themselves scarce — eclipsis and lenition, and tales of seal hunting and the mailman-kings of Great Blasket Island were nothing to the young, born free, or nearly so, as they dreamed of America, of spiffy uniforms, of making money. And later, in the borough of Queens, a narrowback boy learned that *bainne* means milk and *agus* means and, *agus* that was about it. Still later, the narrowback dabbled in Duolingo, learning barely more than enough to say, *Tá brón orm*, I'm sorry.

> *still chasing fox*
> *boy trips on root*
> *hope is on us*

II

You steeled yourselves for trouble, *agus*
for long journeys over water, *agus* you
went, whether fighting *agus* flying as Wild Geese,
or empty-gutted *agus* weeping
in coffin ships, or fire-throated *agus*
under sentence of transport *agus* exile,
or in ocean liners *agus* airplanes, seeking gem-crusted lanes.

We in the wide world forget you, *agus* yet we seek you,
falteringly, stumbling through prayers *agus* rituals,
agus through show-Irish fantasies too fey to mention,
agus through metal agus love shaped into Claddaghs, *agus*, truly,
through the bee-loud words of Yeats *agus* Boland,
agus through Gaeilge, streaming on RTÉ, its strange densities
cut by this tenacious pulse: '*agus... agus... agus...*'

BRIAN O'SULLIVAN

THE VOID

DARA HIGGINS

I woke in the morning and I hated myself. I slouched from bed. I had no choice. The world beguiles with the illusion of choice but really, there's no choice. You work, you buy, you snatch interrupted uneasy sleep, you wake, you do it again. You hate yourself. I hate myself. Why? Last night I ate two Easter eggs. It's not even Easter. I did it in secret, so Tess and the kids wouldn't find out.

I got to work and made a coffee in the kitchenette. Nescafe, instant. Three sugars. Rhona, from the accounts department down the hall, said, 'Three sugars? God, I'd have a headache all day.'

I have a headache most of the time. I assumed it was merely life. The pressure of surfacing every day, like the bends. Her intervention irked me, because that was my mood. The weather irked me. The gradient of the pavement irked me. The buzz of the fluorescent lights irked me.

I said, 'What's it to you?'

She gave me a hurt look, as if *I* had cast aspersions on *her* beverage. She brewed a cup of mint tea and sniffed haughtily, letting me know I was a shithead. I felt bad. Why did I say that? I had nothing against Rhona. Basically, to me, she didn't exist.

Sitting at my desk, my head throbbed and I was uncomfortable. I had to—surreptitiously—undo my belt. The buckle was cutting into my belly. Then I opened the trouser button for a bit of space. If required to stand suddenly my trousers would drop to my ankles. The only reason I could think of for an urgent uprighting would be some kind of emergency, a fire, say. In which case I'd rather sit here at my desk and burn to death, thanks.

On my lunch hour I walked into the city and bought new, larger trousers. And a couple of shirts, size triple-X.

At home, Tess saw the bag. 'I didn't know we were tricking out our wardrobes,' she said. We were watching the finances since the gas company started adding random zeros to our bills.

'I needed some stuff for work,' I said. 'Boring stuff. Shirts and stuff. Cheap.'

I didn't want to tell her I was growing out of my clothes. We couldn't afford my expansion.

At work I tried a coffee with no sugar. It was disgusting, like sipping from a bitter puddle. Who drinks this shit? I threw it into the sink. I would go without coffee. Maybe my head would stop aching?

In my new clothes, I felt at ease. I wasn't sweating. My new trousers didn't itch. The shirt wasn't sticking to my back and I smelled different. I tapped away at the keyboard and my brain wasn't pulsating. I felt weird, I felt okay. Walking to the station I caught sight of my reflection in a shop window. In the billowy strides I looked like Cyril Smith or Ollie Hardy, ludicrous, fat.

I woke in the morning and I hated myself. And still tired. I put on my fat man uniform and avoided reflective surfaces as best I could.

I needed coffee, so stopped by a cafe close to the office. I thought real, brewed coffee, rather than freeze dried scat, might taste okay without the sweetener. The cafe was busy, a line of punters out the door. I ordered, stumbling over my words. Like, a coffee? A black coffee. No sugar. No syrup, no sprinkles, no milk, no soy, nothing but hot water and ground up beans from Colombia or Suriname or Kenya or somewhere else I've never been. It cost me four euro. The barista asked my name.

'Why?'

'For the cup,' he said.

For a stupid second I thought he wanted to introduce me to the cup, that the cup was somehow sentient and needy. I blurted a name that wasn't mine. When they called the name I didn't react. I couldn't remember the name I gave. I left, coffeeless, and got into work ten minutes late. So tired.

At eleven o'clock I cracked. I needed sugary Nescafe. I told myself I'd give it up tomorrow. Rhona was in the kitchenette. She gave me the evil eye so I left, once again sans café. This enmity was apparently a thing. I didn't need it.

I wanted to go to bed the minute I got home but Tess was on lates and I had to feed the kids. I prepared shit food. Oven chips. Processed fish. Mayo, ketchup. When I finished my dinner I finished their leftovers.

Afters was ice cream. I had more than they did.

In the morning I woke, and I hated myself. I had a headache, like a spear of ancient ice wedged between my eyes.

Tess is there in the half light of the bedroom. 'You have to see this.'

She opens the curtains and lets whiteness in. I get out of bed and look out. Snow. Covering every roof for miles. Covering the park. Downstairs the kids laugh as I try to open the back door, but I can't. There's too much snow. A foot, two feet, three! They climb out the window and sink to their knees in the soft snow. No work, no school. Nothing but snow. Food in the larder. A secret stash of mars bars under the stairs. Snowed in until it clears. Could be days. Weeks. Years.

I woke and I hated myself more than usual. As I waited for the train it began to rain. The train, teeming. Inside smelled cloying, damp, sickly. We were jammed up together, wet and miserable, and someone was coughing. Spluttering. Hawking phlegm. Disgusting. I realised it was me.

I waited outside the kitchenette until absolutely sure Rhona wasn't in there. I poured boiling water onto my coffee granules. Three spoons of sugar into the cup and one into my mouth. A colleague left a Cadbury's Flake in the fridge. A woman, obviously. No man would eat a Flake. Apart from me. I stuffed it into my gob. I couldn't taste it.

Later I heard Rhona complaining to a colleague. Her Flake disappeared from the fridge, and she had a fair idea who the culprit was. She had this conversation right next to my cubicle. I wanted to apologise and say I was just desperate. But no good would come from that. I would appear weak, a man who can't be trusted to control his wanton desires.

The next morning there was another Flake in the fridge and I knew it was a trap. I took my sugary coffee to my desk where I had a box of Celebrations in my drawer. They're small, bite sized, so I could pretend I wasn't gorging on them.

I bought some frozen pizzas for dinner. I used to be able to cook, but now I'm too tired. The thought of chopping onions and carrots and frying it all up into a sauce is exhausting. As I paid for my pizzas, on impulse I bought twenty Marlboro. I hadn't smoked in fifteen years. When I smoked I was thinner. Instead of Celebrations and Flakes there were cigarettes.

The price was eye-watering, but it was too late. I lit one as I walked to the child-minder's and I coughed so much I puked into a hedge. After dinner I finished the kids' leftovers, the crusts, the pepperoni. I shoved the pizza wrappings deep in the bin so Tess wouldn't find them.

The headache began before I'd fallen asleep. It persisted all night. When Tess returned and climbed into bed, I was still awake, pretending to be asleep.

In the morning I hated myself. I dropped the kids off and smoked on the way to the train station. It came back to me, the swagger of a cig. How you hold it in your fingers, how you inhale the vapour and blow it out again. The insouciant flick of the butt when finished. I smoked another on the platform. Another as I walked to the office. I took a smoke break at eleven. Before long I needed to buy more. At this rate my new habit was going to cost one hundred euro a week. Tess would kill me before the cancer did.

At home Tess was making goulash with the kids. We ate it with tagliatelle—big, flat noodles. It was so good, such real food, I felt my soul lift. But I helped myself to seconds and mopped it up with bread. My stomach was straining, pained. I ate more, until I was bloated and sweating. Tess put on Lloyd Cole and the Commotions. As she cleaned up, she sang along with Forest Fire. I farted, loud and sudden and long. The kids laughed, as if this was the funniest thing ever. Perhaps it was.

'Jesus, Liam,' she said. 'Have some fucking respect.'

'Language, Tessa,' I said. The kids giggled.

She stopped singing. I liked it when she was singing.

In the old days, when cars were a brand new invention and only the richest, smuggest pricks owned them, a boy would run ahead waving a flag so any serfs on the road would get out of the way. That's what singing is: a signal. Tess shows me she's doing okay with this semaphore—Lloyd, Nina, Kurt. When she's not singing I get anxious, as if at any moment a Thin Lizzy may veer into me at thirty miles an hour.

I farted again. It was a big one. Tess shook her head and blew breath out her nose. I went to the jacks and saw I'd soiled my underwear. I showered, washing myself and my soiled underwear. I tried to cry, but there were no tears.

In bed, Tess told me she'd been horny until the fart. She felt cheapened by my actions. She deserved more than my gas. I agreed with her, but tried to explain it thus: I was in pain. The fart helped me. And in some cultures farting after dinner, *yadda yadda...*

'No sex for you,' she said, and turned her back to me. Maybe she wanted me to beg, but I was relieved. My body was too shameful to share, and the idea of rutting and huffing filled me with dread. I would make things worse by getting on top of her. I'd crush her. And I hadn't had a proper hard-on in a while, which could be an issue. Her breathing thickened and she fell asleep. I stared at the ceiling and felt my own breasts. The sun crept in. I hated myself.

I finished the last of the cigarettes. I wanted more, but I couldn't. I wouldn't. I'd given up. People don't realise how hard it is to give up. I'd done it twice. I'd love to tell Tess. Look at me, free of smokes, but I'd have to first admit I started again. Addiction is difficult.

At eleven o'clock I needed sweet coffee. Rhona was in the kitchenette, as if she fucking lived there. Fuck it. I said hello and she snorted like a mule in a field refusing to take a saddle.

'Oh, fuck off,' I said.

She looked proper put out.

'Yes, I ate your fucking Flake. Tough shit.'

'Why?' She said. There was a girlish hurt in her voice. 'I was looking forward to it.'

I took out my wallet to give her some cash and tell her to go and buy another Flake. A plethora of them. A box of Moro, whatever the fuck, but there was no money in it. Instead I was standing in front of her looking into my empty wallet.

'What are you doing?' she said.

'Do you have a smoke?' I said.

At the end of the month Tess was doing the accounts. She had queries.

'Why did you spend 250 euro on Amazon? What did you buy?'

Difficult to explain, but here goes. I bought boxes of Flakes. Hundreds of the fuckers. I left them everywhere in the office. The fridge. In colleagues' drawers and coat pockets. Hidden among the plastic leaves of our fake plants. I put some behind the radiators where they transmogrified into shapeless masses, no longer the iconic crumbliest, flakiest milk chocolate. I still had boxes of the yokes left over, even after this beneficence. I ate them. I stirred my coffee with Flakes. I gave them to beggars in the street.

'No cash, mate. Do you want a Flake?'

'Not really.'

'Have two.'

'What the fuck are you doing spending so much money on chocolate?' She asked.

'Jesus Christ, Tess. I was doing a good thing.'

'You're not the fucking Easter Bunny, Liam.'

'I can't do anything right can I?'

There was an inquiry. A summons. I reckoned Rhona had ratted me out; she had that vibe, head girl, fun-free, studious and dull, eager to please authority figures. Phyllis wanted to know what the story was with all the Flakes. She didn't get it either.

'I say this from a place of concern, Liam,' said Phyllis. 'You're acting strange. Perhaps you need help.'

Why can't people accept a good deed? Why do they assume there's a nefarious plot afoot, or that wanting to share, wanting to give, is a kind of mental illness?

Tess shook her head at me. 'I'm up to here with this,' she said, without specifying where "here" might be. I didn't know how much space I could yet fill.

'You need help,' she said.

I wake up and I hate myself, what I've done to us. Tess is in the room, by the window.

'You have to see this,' she says.

I look. It's white across the roofs, the trees, the park. We run out into it, laughing and cheering only to discover it isn't snow. It's sugar, a foot deep. Then it rains and the sugar dissolves and it all becomes a syrup. People are stuck in it, trying to pull themselves out. Children scream for caramelised parents.

I woke and I hated myself and my stupid fucking dreams. Tess was not in the room. The children were not in the house. They'd gone to Granny's for the weekend, without me. I got up and drank a litre of milk straight from the carton. The whole thing. Then I ate everything in the fridge. Veg, leftovers, mayonnaise, cheese, raw bacon, half a chorizo sausage, a packet of wilted basil. So much yoghurt. Two cans of beer and half a bottle of Chablis. Numerous carrots. I lay on the floor in a shallow puddle of stomach acids, retching, dying. Doing God's work.

I woke on the tiles, filthy, stinking, a-buzz with self-hate. I slithered into bed like a fat slug. In the morning, I awoke, still rancid, the entire room redolent of puke. I cleaned up and drew a bath. I lay in the tub and imagined drinking the whole thing. Could it be done? I lapped at it, but I lacked the will.

My oldest, only friend, Lacey, phoned. We'd been through the mill in the old days, he and I, when we were drinking. Drink never filled the void, instead it made us aggressive. If, by the end of the evening, we weren't flinging fists into some randomers on the street, we'd start on each other. Lacey still has the scars. We came through it together, scathed, but wiser. We saw less of each other over the years. We married. We procreated. We worked. Lacey was content, nowadays. He was suburban and dressed well. He was fit, lean. On weekends he walked hills. He played five a side. He had a mistress and a motorbike, and his wife knew about neither.

'Tess called me,' he said. 'She's worried, and I am too, mate.'

He told me to meet him in a bar in town for a proper chat. The bar sold many IPAs and chicken wings. I was on my second plate when he arrived.

He said, after small talk eked away, 'Did you ever consider therapy?'

I said, 'Of course not. That's why we drink, isn't it?'

'It's not so bad,' he said, sounding like he was trying to convince himself. But, let's say this for Lacey: his eyes were clear and he listened to me intently. He was lean, and confident. 'It gets better,' he insisted. 'Things change.'

I didn't believe him. The void persists. What is more permanent than an immense nothingness?

Lacey's watch was heavy on his wrist, expensive, counting seconds as if they were weightless. His suit was expertly cut. His hairline was receding but his pate was polished. He looked like a man who understood the world. I didn't really recognise him. We drank, regardless. What else was there to do?

I woke, and I hated myself. This time, on the couch, fully clothed. One shoe on. One shoe elsewhere. I couldn't find it in the house. My brain was trying to punch its way out of my skull. I guzzled water from the kitchen tap, metallic and lukewarm, to slake an unquenchable thirst. My knees hurt and my clothes were dirty, as if I'd been rolling around the streets. At some stage the evening dissolved into a blackness. Wings, Lacey, booze, pub, blackness, couch. I didn't really have any desire to fill in the blanks. There would be nothing to learn from it.

As I emptied my pockets to wash my clothes I found a business card. Bent, stained, the colour of a rain cloud, embossed with the words: *Dr Nicolas Paul. Therapist.* An address, but no number. Where had it come from? I didn't know. Lacey? Maybe. Or maybe I'd picked it up in a phone booth, like in the old days in London when the boxes were plastered in little cards promising much delight. Back then I'd looked at them and never managed to muster the courage to call. So many potential massages, missed.

I held the card and thought to myself; what if this is fated? What if this is the moment everything changes. I can't fully explain it. I was terribly hungover, the kind of malaise where everything seems like it will be the last time I'll ever do it and I should make sure my will is in order. Put it this way. I was out of options.

The doctor's office was above a nail salon, on an ill-appointed, litter-bejewelled back street. Stabbings were entertainment here. Graffiti was illiterate and profuse. I ascended the stairs and into his office. It was fine: a nice carpet, a bookshelf stacked with leather clad tomes, comfortable chairs. It looked cosy and smelled of incense.

The doctor introduced himself. 'Nicolas Paul,' he said, holding out a chamois-soft hand. He smelled good, he deported himself like the leader of a small, mineral rich country. He checked my credentials.

'Do you know Lacey?' I asked. He made a subtle head movement that may or may not have been a nod, it was hard to tell.

He said. 'What's your history with him?'

I potted it. As children we grew up in good homes, free of stress, with space and energy to play all day, excited for the next day and the one after. The world was abundant with mystery there in the gluey past. Which is why it's so hard to accept this sullen lump I've become. I didn't have the excuse of abuse or poverty or stupidity. As we got older, we found our world constricted. There was less and less of it, fewer mysteries. We drank, to invent stories. We fought, in desperation. We attempted to fuck, with varying degrees of success. We entered adulthood, horrified at the world created for us. The nature and joy of our youth replaced by the drudge and concrete of work.

'Life,' I told Doctor Paul, 'is a drag.'

'The problem,' he told me, 'is you can see life for what it is. Most people trundle along, unaware of the con. You remember the freedom of primal youth, swimming and climbing and throwing stones at pensioners. Adulthood was invented by capitalists.'

That was the gist anyway, I was half listening. My stomach rumbled. My eyes hurt. Why was I here?

He went into another room and returned a minute later with a china bowl. Chunks of meat in some kind of soy based sauce. Blackened and salty. It smelled pretty good, but once I ate half a toilet roll in the work toilets to see if I could, so I was hardly an epicurean.

'Garlic, soy sauce, sesame seeds,' he said. 'Simple, yes. The meat needs little adornment. It will fill the hole in you. Full of protein and all that is good. Once you have mastered your craving, you can concentrate on whatever you want. My clients include business people, politicians, ordinary folk who want to live free of want. Film stars have graced my presence. Everyone you see is suffering because no one knows what we're supposed to be doing. I realised many years ago that to succeed you need to be free of ordinary travails. Now, don't get me wrong, success isn't money, or power, unless you want it to be. Success is peace to reach one's potential. To achieve.'

He spoke while I ate my third piece of meat, my fingers sticky. The meat was ok: a bit tough. Chewy. The sauce was unctuous. It was unremarkable but I ate. The bowl was half full still when I realised I was no longer hungry. I looked at the food. I wanted to eat it because it was there, I'd never left a plate un-cleared, but I felt... *full.*

'I can tell by the look on your face it has already worked.'

'What's going on?' I said.

He handed me a wet-wipe from a plastic pack on his desk and I cleaned my fingers. I looked at him, and saw him as if for the first time. His face was too smooth, his teeth too white. He exuded vanity. The cut of his shirt was exquisite. He was the most confident person I'd ever met. He had my attention in its fullest. I felt weird. He leaned towards me, his breath, minty and clinical.

'What you've eaten is human flesh.'

The words should have jolted me into some kind of insanity, but his revelation didn't come as a surprise. I nodded languidly, as if he'd told me it would rain later.

'Your transformation has begun. Once you've tasted man, or woman, you can never go back.'

'I see,' I said.

I wake and Tess is in the room. She opens the curtains and says, come, quick, and I get up and look out. Blood, everywhere, a tsunami of it. The roofs of the houses are painted maroon. The garden, a lake of gore. The kids are jumping off the trampoline into the blood and re-emerging, covered in it. 'Look, daddy. Look at us.'

I woke and I was alone and I laughed at my stupid fucking dream. On the nose, much? In the bathroom I weighed myself. Some big numbers flashed up on the LCD. I laughed. I left the house and ran to the train station. When had I last run? I couldn't remember. My lungs burned and my ankles ached, but it felt good. There was the usual crush on the train, but I waded into their midst as if they were long grass, flattened by my step. I was sweating, glowing, no doubt smelling from my exertion. I didn't care.

Work was easy. My job was dumb. It was about procrastination. Putting clients off, finding reasons not to do things. I wrote a macro in Excel and finished a month's work in the morning. In the afternoon I walked about the office stalking potential quarry.

To complete my therapy I had to hunt and kill one victim, and then eat their flesh—raw, cooked, off the bone, in a curry, it didn't matter. Once accomplished I'd have ascended to the realm of superman. No longer a mere mortal. I knew somewhere in my consciousness all this was bollocks, but I felt good about myself, which was novel and rewarding. People believe all kinds of shit in order to get through the day. God, and all that ordure. Eternal reward, reincarnation, karma, whatever. You can believe in the essential goodness of humans, and that's a swizz. People are garbage. We're all animals, scurrying about, clawing at each other, trying to fuck and fuck each other over, picking on the weak, voting for the bastards, hoarding resources. When you get down to it, the species isn't worth saving.

I was in the kitchenette making myself a camomile and manuka tea, the desire for sugar having disappeared, when in walked Rhona. It was her, surely. She was, somehow or other, my sworn enemy. I would feast on her, suck the marrow from her bones, make tartar of her breasts. I smiled at her, and she in return gave me that withering glance I had become accustomed to. I savoured it, for the last time.

'See you later,' I said as I left.

At night I dressed in black. I felt lean, although I wasn't. I moved silently on my toes. I was armed with the sharpest of knives from our kitchen drawer. It was still pretty blunt. I'd rip the flesh with my teeth, if need be. With the hot scent of dinner in its nostrils, did a wolf dither over the cutlery?

Like mine, Rhona's house was a dull suburban lump. I climbed the back wall and dropped into the garden, obscured by the bushes and the shed and obfuscating darkness. From here, crouched and invisible, I was able to scope her kitchen through the double glass doors. It was a bright movie screen in the dark. I felt incredibly present in the moment. I was a predator. A beast.

Rhona walked into the scene and opened the fridge, took out a bottle of wine, filled a glass. Her kitchen was sterile, like a showroom. Not the heart of a home. No kid's art on the fridge, no stains on the wall. I watched her leave. I moved closer to peek in the window of the sitting room. I heard the television. Brian Cox was bellowing. She was watching *Succession*, laughing at something on the screen. I peeked discreetly into the room. She was on the couch, the glass of wine on the coffee table in front of her. She was lying against, you may say snuggled up to, a man. He had his arms around her shoulder. They watched television. Roman did a thick thing. Shiv was selfish. The couple laughed. How long was I there, it's hard to tell. But the credits rolled, the show over, and they turned their attention from the television to each other, kissing, handsy. Still I watched. Who was this guy? Rhona had never struck me as the kind of woman who would have a beau. This Rhona on the couch, with such abandon pawing at her fella, was no Rhona I knew. Where was the pettiness, the obsession with confection, the tattle telling? This woman was carnal, limber. This Rhona, a stranger to me, had the athletic body of a dancer, maybe, or a gymnast. I imagined the hours put into a craft, the dedication and sacrifice. The love of sport or performance. Perhaps a career thwarted by the dull monotony of bills and work. I'd never considered her in any particular way before, never looked directly at her. She had a hinterland within her, a place foreign to me, swamped in the marshes of my own self-loathing as I was. Rhona, human and vulnerable, but strong and forceful, making her man come like a stallion, right there on the couch, illuminated by the glare of the television. This Rhona was atop her life, grinding pleasure from it, gloriously alive. She was, in all ways, more worthy of living than I, peeping through the window with a blunt knife from Ikea in my sweating paw. Me, the beast. The alpha. The clarity with which I'd seen the world in the previous few days dissolved into a murky mist.

I woke, and hated myself. I smelled badly. I was sleeping beside some bins next to a restaurant. The speciality of the diner was burnt grease, if the contents of their bin was anything to go by. A limp sky spat half-hearted rain. I was ensconced across from the office of Doctor Nicolas Paul and my mission was to kill him. And possibly eat him? No, merely to kill him. He was an insidious worm who fed me mistruth and caused me to consider appalling things. I waited for a day, a second day. I hid behind the bins any time a human ventured by, usually the KP's having a smoke and gabbing in Portuguese. I admired their camaraderie and cigarettes, the simplicity of work and smoking and laughing and life being lived with their nonchalant, youthful vigour.

I slept badly on a piece of cardboard. Rain was constant. Rats for company. On the third day it was clear Paul wasn't returning. Grabbing initiative by its horns, I entered his building and broke into office.

It wasn't sophisticated. I kicked the door until it splintered. The office was completely denuded. No couch, no carpet, no tomes. Nothing but blank walls and naked floorboards and a bulb hanging from a wire like it had taken its own life. Somehow, this was the denouement I expected. I was weak with tiredness and a hunger I'd truly earned. I headed home.

I woke, and felt indifferent about myself. Tess stood by the window. 'Come and see,' she said.

I got out of bed and looked. Nothing. The roofs and park and roads, as they always were. 'What?' I said.

'The kids,' she said.

There they were, cavorting in the garden, bouncing on the trampoline, laughing. Every day was an adventure to them. Imagine going to bed excited at what mysteries the morning might bring.

'You're home,' I said to Tess. 'I missed you.'

She fixed me with a serious look, as if considering something removed from a patient. Was I malignant? Could I be cured?

'I can't go back to the way it was,' she said.

'It can never be the way it was, ever again,' I said. 'But that's okay.'

Together we looked out the window. She snaked her arm about my waist.

'You've lost weight,' she said.

'It's this new diet,' I said. 'Human flesh.'

She laughed and squeezed my flab.

'You haven't cracked a joke in so long,' she said.

I kissed her, and she kissed me, and I heard her breathing through her nose. Her beautiful, sweet breath, her soft skin. Each bone of her I know better than I know myself.

'I'm sorry,' I said.

Outside, thick flakes of snow started to fall across the roofs, the park, the garden. The kids wailed with pleasure.

COMMUTER

We run two or three degrees cooler than our dawnbreak counterparts,
me and everyone else running late, our blood moving steady.
There are seats if we want them, and we all have iced coffees
and laughter in the throat as we chat with a friend
already on probation with their manager.
Voice over the intercom says the train is taking a breather.
Construction, improvements, and all that.
We roll our shoulders back and sigh, eyes drifting up
to the sky still hazy from last night's low lightning.
The man across the aisle is reading the folded-over
page of the book in my hands;
I hold it aloft a little longer so he can finish.

ELIZABETH O'CONNELL-THOMPSON

FUCK ART

The poetry prompt asks you
to write about someone you love
so much you'd eat them,
gnaw the tibia to a quill,
the jawline to a crime scene,
into a shot of you being hauled
into the Special Criminal Court,
hands cuffed, jacket over the head type shit.
     Invoke the senses to engage the reader.
Think lemon in the brain,
acid dancing inside the ear,
when you look into their eyes
do you see the church burning on a hill?
     Write the weather
above the last place you fucked,
the sky static with flies sucking salt
like democracy off your foreheads.
     Write the truth,
where it really happened,
the wallpaper of the HAP scheme bedsit,
its archive of cigarettes,
blu-tacked posters of Cobain,
the 27 club rendered in lung-yellow.
     The aim of this exercise is to remember
what your mother's perfume smelled like,
the way she'd scrub a dock leaf on her stings
and said this was the medicine of fields.
     Dress your poem in nature,
adopt the persona of a pig discovering
the idea of itself, pink reflections in the trough
before you turn to shove your snout
into your dead piglet

and become yourself again.
          Try your hand at dramatic monologue.
Unzip the back of a stranger
and wear them
like a pervert behind a curtain.
          Write forgiveness
for lying to the person
who really loved you,
invoke the mattress,
its cartography of cum,
its star-map of want saying:
Fuck!
I love you,
I love your hatred of antiques.
Your tongue inside my mouth
is a cup of milk,
is the dogs asleep
and a walk along the canal in June.
          Write the little depression after climax,
that moment of numbness
like when you walk out of a cinema
at night.
          Write your home
where the body isn't fetish
for the car crash through your garden,
the chewed ampersand of a spine
and a ditch growing louder
with the Mazda's of young men,
          Write friendship
as being questioned
to the attempted shooting on your mate,
whose income was a spoon of tar
stitched inside an arm,
whose goodbye wasn't a picture of him
boarding a flight
but the sawn-off misfiring in the wall

like starlings twisting into Spain.
          Write your last poem.
What you really mean.
Kill the birds and just say
I don't want to die alone,
real tulips are waiting
just above the page,
the screen,
sugar igniting on the leaves,
actual honey dripping
from a bee's spine.
          Now,
click submit on your trauma poem.
Wish acceptance as exiting stage left
through the wrists
with its red curtains
and lavender candles,
pour yourself a drink
and glide a knife along
your least favourite artery,
for those five minutes
you'll take nothing for granted.
          Write that poem.
If not for yourself,
for me.

SIMON COSTELLO

GARTH BROOKS DRIVE BY

To ease the pain, you clamp the bloody tissue
to your jaw as we huddle on the steps

of the Four Courts, waiting for Kavanagh's bus.
Your back tooth pulled for free, by an apprentice

dentist in the hospital at the back of Trinity. I stood
beside your stretched mouth, full of blood

and empty of anesthetic as he wrenched it free.
Off the Liffey the wind howls in our faces

as a stretch limo creeps towards the docks
ferrying the king of country to his throne

followed by wave upon wave of steadfast fans
a sea of Stetson's and cowboy boots. With false

bravado we congratulate ourselves —
we're too cool for country music.

BARBARA DUNNE

IF YOU HAVE EVER BEEN DETAINED IN A POLICE STATION OVERNIGHT

you will know that the room you are detained in has no windows. I was once arrested for being in possession of a Class A drug. After dropping a tab of acid, my teenage boyfriend jumped through the window of our second floor flat onto the street below. What I remember most was the hours spent staring at the cell door until the pattern of the wood-grain transmuted into an Alsatian dog.

It's not yet a crime to stare through windows, nor a crime for windows to stare at us. Transparency is a virtue after all. Some scientists believe that there's an inherent subjective experience of consciousness in even the tiniest particle, like the sand that goes into the making of glass. The safest windows to stare through are those that allow you in such as florists, department stores with yet to be dressed mannequins, tube trains about to depart.

When I was ten my brother called me a weirdo for staring at people in church. I have two daughters. Both have told me I mustn't stare at their new boyfriends. I have learnt it is safer to stare at stars.

It is acceptable to stare at a baby's face, at sunsets and sunrises, grasshoppers rubbing their legs, the Mona Lisa. If you stare long enough at a pink spot on a sheet of white paper affixed to your bedroom wall a green aura will appear. This too is acceptable.

Yesterday, an acquaintance at a writing workshop told me that the son of a woman there fell from a window in Dublin. *Window* happened to be one of the random words I had called out, along with *ghost, fire, sand* and *trees*, as prompts for the imagination.

It's not acceptable to stare at the recently bereaved, breastfeeding mothers on trains, naked men on the beach, those in wheelchairs, people with facial tics, car accidents, or women's breasts. Just recently posters have been put up in tube stations around the city stating: *Intrusive staring of a sexual nature is sexual harassment and is not tolerated.* A man was sentenced to twenty-two weeks in prison after a woman reported him for continuously staring at her on a train in Berkshire.

A senior British Transport Police Officer admitted that it's human nature to stare at things. This morning I spotted three men in raincoats sitting on a bench at Hilsea Halt, jotting down serial numbers of passing trains. Sometimes it's difficult to avert your gaze.

MAGGIE SAWKINS

TELOS

ALAN EGAN

When it's your turn in the butts, the targets look huge. Unmissable, surely. Sheets of canvas stretched on timber frames about the size of the big front windows in the new houses out in Bishopstown, the whole oper- ation resembling the rope and pulley system they use to change bits of background scenery in the theatre on South Main Street. Haul them up, haul them down, again and again, hand over hand with the ropes, a drudge of a task, especially when you're on the bleak mountainside near Kilworth and the grey mist is soaking your greatcoat.

They're up right now, the line of targets all along the trench, and you stand there in the appointed position, your new polished army boots maybe eight feet below ground level, waiting for the crisp sound of rifle- fire. Behind is a big bank of earth, how many bullets are lodged in there? Even thinking about a quick search might get you shot, by accident or by design.

You hear the barked order in the distance, maybe 200 yards away, then the sporadic cracks of gunshot. An 'In your own time, fire' command. In the quietness that follows, the sergeant at the end of the line flicks his flag and you lower the target. Your sidekick comes over. He's a private also but he's done more time than you, two stars on his sleeves, so he's the one entrusted to find the bullet holes, maximum five for this drill. Five little holes in a big ancient canvas sheet. Easy or almost impossible, it depends on the rifleman, who might be a mate of your sidekick so you've been ordered to make sure there's no monkey business, no peeling off an old patch or two to improve a score, no sir.

Some shooters are shit-hot, you think, the five holes pretty much dead centre, all in a group, all within a few inches of each other. Hitting the middle of the target is one thing, but the grouping is what it's all about. So you watch your sidekick locating each of the five, or maybe only three of four, and noting the score, which the sergeant checks. And then you're there with a well-used brush and a jar of mucky adhesive and a supply of small square canvas patches, and you hold the jar while Mister Two-Star Private pastes a fresh patch over each bullet hole. Then the pair of you step back smartly into position and stand to rigid attention, waiting for the next order to hoist them up again.

And you're here because this is a Field Day, most likely it's a Sunday, and you're a dogsbody, but you're loving it, aren't you?

Some other Sunday, after you've spent weeks and weeks pounding every square inch of the massive Collins' Barracks square into submission, and you've practised how to strip and reassemble a rifle, and a Bren gun, and then how to do it again and again, blind-folded and in less than thirty seconds. And when you can do all that there's another Field Day on the schedule, although they rarely tell you where you're going or why.

But you're back in Kilworth, and this time you're away down the range, looking at those targets from 100, 200, 300 yards away and they seem tiny. Unhittable.

When you enlisted you lied about your age, of course you did, same as the other lads, but the sergeant who came to the school didn't bat an eyelid, did he? So now you're here, and thank God it's a dry Sunday, though bloody cold, and you're fifteen years old, and you lie spread-eagled, on your elbows, your forearms touching the sandbag, the pre-WW2 Lee Enfield .303 in your hands. It has a bolt action mechanism and five live rounds in the spring-loaded magazine, and going round in your head is the mantra: first-pressure, hold, second-pressure, squeeze, bang, recoil. You've never before fired a live round. You've never before felt that kick into your shoulder, some of the older lads telling you they'd put bits of folded blanket inside their uniform, and maybe you might do that too at some stage, but would you then miss the feel of it, maybe you and your rifle might feel separated?

'Five rounds, in your own time, fire!'

Fair enough, you're thinking, but your pause before second pressure was maybe too long and the crack was louder and the recoil really kicked and you're thinking the way she jerked, that first round must have cleared the entire bank of earth behind the butts, never mind the target.

But after that, with the other four, it all feels a bit smoother. Yeah.

So you store all of it into your memory bank, every bit of it, the flicking off of the safety catch, the setting of your sights, your eye along the barrel, and then the magic of it, the thrill of it, a live deadly .303 bullet flying to its target. Then it's bolt-up, pull back, bright brass cartridge ejected, next round up, sliding snugly in place as you push the bolt forward and locked down again, ready for your next shot with this well-oiled tried and tested piece of killing equipment.

Only then do you realise the horror.

The order is given to move back up to the 100 yard mark. You fall into line with the rest of the platoon, and you can control your movements, but not your thoughts.

Spread-eagled once more, on another sandbag, they nag.

Have bullets from this rifle, this actual rifle nestling against your cheek, have they killed people? Surely not, after all, this is the FCA, and you're only a one-day-a-week soldier, and this is the Irish Army: we don't kill people, do we? It's all just a drill, isn't it? Then you remember Sergeant Connie Martin, all five-foot-nothing of him, not long back from the Belgian Congo with his matter-of-fact Cork accent and his stories of Katanga, and Baluba tribesmen, and that vicious bloody battle where nobody knows exactly how many died in total and that's a true story, isn't it? And Corporal Donoghue, that little bollix, explaining the histories of the Bren guns and the Lee Enfields and how almost all of them belonged to the British army at one time or another, who knows who fired them and at whom: maybe 'Tans murdering your ancestors, or Irishmen killing Irishmen in the Civil War, and those stories are true too, yeah?

You feel this weapon, randomly handed to you earlier when you jumped down from the back of the Bedford 3-ton army truck with its canvas stretched tight across the frame over the timber benches; you feel this Lee Enfield .303, its timber stock warm against your cheek, the slick mechanism, the symmetry of the five lethal rounds, and more in your pouch, and you're fifteen years old and you're remembering Buddy, your Latin teacher who's also a Greek scholar, and his talk of Aristotle and how everything in the world has a telos, a unique purpose without which it wouldn't exist. And the telos of this piece of equipment is simply and solely to kill people, no question about it. And you consider, in this crazy world of 1961 with the Reds and the Yanks ready to literally go ballistic over each other, you consider how many millions of these killing machines exist, all similar yet all individual, each with their own story. Yes, each rifle with its own killing history, and you wonder how many men or women caressed this particular trigger and with a final squeeze sent another messenger of death hurtling on its way to strike who or what. God only knows.

A hundred yards away, you hear the creaking targets being hauled up once more.

The next order will be 'Five rounds, rapid fire' and you know that your solitary job now is to reach the required number of hits in the short time allotted, the number required to earn the star, your very first red and yellow star, the one that you long to sew onto and to proudly display on the arm of your tunic.

And so you obey.

THERE'S NO WAR IN CALABASAS

I've always had a tendency to self-destruct,
smoking was my favorite crutch,
I loved it so much, but had to give it up.

Used to drink to excess but that was messy,
so I traded it in for sobriety.

Now, I have a new habit, maybe worse than the rest,
I might regret sharing this, but sometimes,
I watch The Kardashians.

I know, it's not rational,
this klan of fashion, greed, and monstrous superficiality
should be against all I stand for.

But watching their nonsense numbs my frontal cortex,
like a soothing lullaby,
their vocal fry sedates me into a state of basic bliss.

There's no war in Calabasas,
no climate crisis, no ongoing inequality, there's just vanity.

The only thing that holds gravity is taking the perfect selfie,
and for a minute, I'm shifted into this alternate reality.

Bewitched into suddenly giving a shit if Kim can fit
into her dress for the Met Ball.

It's so awfully shallow and dumb, like, 26 year old Kendall,
couldn't cut a cucumber by herself, she had to call Chef to do it.

Yet these are who young women are to consider aspirational.
Sure, they have their own personal tribulations,
but we never see that stuff, because it's not glamorous.

Instead, we are ravenous peasants lining up for a Dionysus
of boobs, bronzer, and private jets.

Their cares are all inconsequential because at the end of the day,
they have so much fame and money that nothing is a problem
for them. It's complete escapism.

Yes, they promote disordered eating, and every new season
their facial features migrate like a Picasso portrait,
to the extent it's difficult telling which one is which,
but that's part of the fun.

They're like a coven of witches,
Triple Hecates' of hair extensions, lip fillers, and contouring knickers.

Ultra-femme vikings who infiltrated a vapid culture.
Their mother, Kris Jenner, the guardian of a beige Valhalla,
Hall of the Slay'n.

Day in, day out, brands are endorsed
and they have forced their way into our brains.

The muses of materialism.
The sirens of consumerism.

The hot girls of the apocalypse.
The true sign of the end times.

People say they are stupid but I dispute this,
it is we, their audience, who are in fact the idiots
for watching them.

THERE'S NO WAR IN CALABASAS

I know, it's a problem.
I'm just a recreational user but it's a slippery slope.
I hope I can kick the habit.

So, there we have it:
Forgive me, for I have sinned,

I keep up with the Kardashians.

SHAUNNA LEE LYNCH

PIGEON

I remember the people in my town.
There was *Ten to Two*, who walked like Charlie Chaplin
and *Tabernacle O'Connor*, the priest's favourite.
There was *Giro*, who stole a cheque from the Credit Union,
and *Slab Sullivan*, whose father ran the concrete works.
There was *Beans* and his brother *Chips*,
and *Sunday World*, who had all the news.

And then there was me, *Pigeon*.
I believed them when they said a bird
got sucked into the combined harvester.
They smeared droppings on my books in school
and flapped their arms when I walked by with my brothers.
I left town after secondary and went to work in Dublin.
When I come home I stay on the outskirts
avoiding the pubs and nightclubs,
afraid some local drunk will recognise me
and shout after me in the street.

COLM SCULLY

FRIDAY AT 19 UPPER FRIARS ROAD

For Mary Cahill

On the crest of the city a young man stops
before a slight terraced house.
Startled by laughter that bulges
out the door. He rings the bell.

How are ya boy?

Uncle Noel, youngest of the twelve, leads him
through a hall that seems to shrink with each step.
He stoops through the kitchen door, squeezes past
aunts, uncles, second cousins once removed.
Slapped and shook, stamped with lips. Led to his
grandmother who accepts a kiss on a cold cheek.

Sit down there

Hunched at the hob, in her altered chair, she lifts
a dripping peeled spud from the pot, examines it,
starts to cut. The small blade nestled beneath
her index finger, she works the sharp edge
through, hitting the board with a muffled

    knock

           knock

                      knock

careful incisions made with her good hand,
the other laid across her lap. Knuckle and bone,

swollen and fused. From her elevated seat
she conducts a team of mouthy servers with nods,
eyebrows, a few words. She drops the cut potato
into the deep fat, sending up a roar. Spatters fly but
she doesn't flinch. She breaks an egg into the pan.
The young man sits dazed in the din as Noel tries
to get a rise out of her. Hands bang the table,
chair legs scrape as bodies contort with laughter.

D'ya hear him?

she says, eyes thrown to the ceiling.
She shakes the fat off the chips, slides on the egg,
nods to the table. Noel serves with fake panache.
The young man stares at the plate, salivates.
The chips glisten, all edges, stacks of golden
treasure piled around a white globe, its yellow core.

He bursts the yolk, it spills through the crowded plate.

EOIN CAHILL

ONE MOMENT

One moment I'm walking home under stars so bright
        no flashlight is needed,

next I'm ducking into a neighbour's banger
        as hail pounds down

and whitens the night and I'm grateful
        islanders don't lock their cars.

Fatherly smell of pipe tobacco in the snug, dark VW.
        A staccato clatter surrounds me.

And just like that it's over and I'm walking again
        beneath brilliant stars,

Cape Clear spread out beneath me as I ponder
        the just-like-that-ness of the world.

One moment I'm dining with my parents
        in Galway's Pasta Paradiso,

revelling in the spicy main course, Road to Hell.
        Next moment

both parents are gone. Even the restaurant. Gone.
        Like a constellation

linked by imagined lines, I join moment
        to moment, making a story

that becomes this life in which I walk fast,
        leave doors unlocked,

strive to stay grateful, and keep glancing at the cloud
that's already blurring the western sky.

THEODORE DEPPE

SUMMER IS ENDING IN BARROW-IN-FURNESS

ROSEMARY JOHNSTON

And so it was that to end off the summer, Jenna would ask Louie if he'd like to have a mum and son weekend away. But Louie's choice was always to have his mates round, camping in the garden. Like many aspects of having a teenage son, the camping weekend annoyed and pleased Jenna in equal measure. She would spend the whole weekend worrying about the lads doing back flips off the trampoline into the paddling pool. And somehow, attracted by a scent or something, the local girls always turned up in push-up bras and flip flops. Last year, to keep the half-naked girls warm, the boys used the barbecue as a stove and put so many logs in it, they melted the bowl.

So this year, again, when she asked him what he wanted to do with their weekend, she expected him to choose camping.

Louie looked up from his phone. He hadn't shaved or bothered with a haircut, so he looked like Lon Chaney Jr. in *The Wolf Man*.

'Town are playing away in Barrow,' he said. 'We could go and watch the game?'

'Football in August?'

'It's the start of the season.'

'Don't you want to get the tent down out of the attic?' Jenna asked. Football in Barrow seemed even worse than the camping.

The boys would sleep all morning, having been up till 6 a.m. scrolling TikTok. And when she heard them stirring late morning, she'd start cooking breakfast for them. Sausages, bacon, eggs, fried onions, a whole loaf of toast. They didn't actually eat food, it was just fuel they shovelled into the fire pit of their stomachs.

'Everyone's away,' Louie said. Was that really it, or had they outgrown the tent?

Barrow. All she knew of it was that it was an unattractive shipbuilding town. She got out her laptop. What to do in Barrow. It turned out there was a nature reserve on Walney Island, the Irish sea, a not bad hotel, and a decent pub. That would do.

She told Louie she had thought about it and was prepared to go.

'Seriously?' he said. 'We're really going to go?'

'I'll drive us over on Saturday morning, watch the match, stay the night in a hotel.'

'I wanted to go on the supporters' bus.'

'Supporters' bus?'

'For the experience.'

'But what sort of experience?' she asked, aghast. 'It's my weekend away, too.' She thought for a moment. 'I tell you what, if I agree to go on the supporters' bus, will you agree to go and look at the nature reserve after the match?'

'Nature reserve?'

'Yeah,' she said. 'Birds. Sand dunes.'

'You're joking?' He fell down on the floor and lay on it, convulsing, like Frankenstein's monster. He put out his leg as if to kick her. It reminded her of that time she had displeased him and he'd given her a sly kick on the shin, as if she was a tethered beast of burden, too meek to react. He knew better these days, but she could see he still thought about it.

'No. That's the deal. You get the football match. I get the birding.'

'Birding!' he wailed. 'Jenna, Jenna, Jenna—why are you my mother?'

'How do you get the tickets?'

'There's a guy called Jason, he runs the supporters' club.'

Later, Louie told her he had booked the tickets, and two places on the coach.

'But when I told Jason we didn't want to come back he asked me to tell you to ring him.'

'Did you tell him you were going with your mum?'

'Yes. There's his number.'

'He probably didn't believe you,' Jenna laughed.

She rang Jason and told him she was indeed Louie's mum and, no, they didn't want to come back on the bus and, yes, they were staying the night in Barrow. He accepted her explanation and told her that a local club near Morecambe had offered to provide lunch. She didn't think she would enjoy the lunch provided by the local club. She would make a packed lunch for herself. She booked the first train back.

On the morning of the match, she packed a change of clothing, soap bag, and a raincoat in a cabin bag. She took it downstairs, told Louie to bring his stuff to put in it. He was wearing a black and yellow Town scarf and a Town baseball cap.

'You can't bring that,' said Louie, pointing in horror at the cabin bag.

'Why not?'

'You don't go to a football match with a purple suitcase.'

'I think there's a black one too. I could see if I could find that?'

'No suitcase. I'll look like a right twat. Minimise. It's one night.'

She sighed and shoved a change of underwear and a toothbrush into a backpack. She put the sandwich she had prepared in it. She told Louie to get his own backpack and to pack a coat, the forecast wasn't great, he'd need it for the nature reserve.

'It's the hottest summer on record. I don't need a coat.'

'The hottest summer on record is coming to an end this weekend,' she said. 'And go shave, for God's sake.'

They walked up to the ground where the coach awaited them. There were about forty supporters, young and old, mostly men, but a few women.

'Don't speak to anybody,' Louie said. 'Anybody at all.'

'Which one is Jason?' Jenna asked. Louie nodded to a balding man in his fifties. Seeing them look at him, Jason came over.

'Your first time joining us?'

'Yes,' she said. 'Louie has been to a lot of the matches, but this is my first!'

'It can get a bit, well...' Jason hesitated, 'noisy. And there can be a bit of language.'

'It's okay, I'll cope.'

And sure enough, on cue, a young man in Town colours joggers and a Town shirt and scarf started chanting.

'Oh Town! Mighty, mighty Town!' He conducted a group of lads who echoed 'Mighty, mighty Town!' at the tops of their voices.

'That's Moxy. He's always here.'

They kept up the chanting as everyone boarded the bus.

Louie sat down, his chest and shoulders filled the seat like a sandy haired St. Bernard, his biceps nudging Jenna out of the way. Jenna perched on the edge of her seat. He looked at her out of the corner of his eye. She could see he was wondering how much of this she would be able to take.

The bus set off. She tried to read the weekend papers as the chanting and the hissing sound of tins of lager being pulled opened filled the bus. Every time the bus rounded a corner, she had to put her foot down on the aisle to stop herself falling off the seat.

'Do people actually like this?'

'You like a drink.'

'Not at 10 in the morning, I don't.'

'I hope you're not going to complain the whole time. You agreed to come.'

Even a repeat of the year it had poured down the whole camping weekend would have been preferable. The boys spent the evening inside playing on the Xbox, only leaving the house at 1 a.m., crisscrossing the garden carrying sleeping bags and pillows. Jenna watched them from the bedroom window as they tried to zip up the tent's outer door. If they didn't get it closed, the entire inside of the tent would be soaked. She went out to help them, standing in the sodden garden in her jammies, pushing and pulling the damn zip, while the rain lashed her, the boys dry inside, holding a torch for her. It took her a week to dry out the sleeping bags.

After what felt like several hours, the bus turned off the main road, down towards Morecambe.

'Look,' she said to Louie. He didn't react so she tapped him on the arm. He took his headphones off. Out of them came a sports' commentator's voice. She pointed out the Cumbrian peaks that could be seen to the north-west. 'The journey back tomorrow will be beautiful, the train line passes right along the coast down to Lancaster, then across the Western Dales. Some of the best scenery in England.'

Louie listened, then put his headphones back on.

The bus turned along the coast road. The swirling eddies of Morecambe Bay glistened. She tapped Louie on the shoulder. 'Look,' she said, 'the Irish Sea.'

He reluctantly removed his headphones, but otherwise appeared uninterested.

'A tragedy happened in this bay a few years ago.'

She carried on despite seeing Louie brace himself for one of her stories.

'A group of Chinese people, illegal immigrants—they'd been trafficked here—they were sent out to harvest cockles at low tide. But they didn't understand the tides and they were cut off when the tide came in. About twenty of them drowned.'

Telling the story brought tears to her eyes and this seemed to affect Louie because tears welled up in his eyes too. He looked out of the window, towards the choppy, grey Irish sea. Clouds were building on the horizon.

'Such a tragedy.'

'Fuck sake,' said Louie. 'Why do you always have to tell me these terrible stories?'

'I thought you'd be interested.'

'Why would I be interested? It's such a grim story about people drowning! We're on the supporters away day. It's supposed to be fun!'

'Oh,' she said.

He didn't understand the way she saw the world, dismaying at her tendency towards the tragic, the macabre, even.

The bus pulled into the car park of the local football club. Everyone got off the bus and piled into the clubhouse and stood three deep at the bar. Each table had as its centrepiece a large bowl of crisps. Jenna sat at one of them. Pints were pulled and handed over. Horse racing on the telly. Jenna told Louie to go and get himself some food.

He stood at the bar and returned with a lemonade.

'Did you get me a drink?'

'I didn't know you wanted one.'

'What food did you get?'

'They've only got hotdogs.'

'You like hotdogs.'

'It's those tinned frankfurters.'

'Oh.'

Jenna sighed and took the sandwich, which had she cut into four, out of her backpack and shared it with Louie. He ate two of the sandwiches in two bites.

'Have another one,' she said, reluctantly.

'It's okay.'

'I'm not really hungry,' she lied.

'They'll have pork pies and sausage rolls at the ground,' he said, taking a third sandwich.

'Great.'

At the ground she climbed some concrete steps and sat on a hard square of coloured plastic that was screwed to another block of concrete. Louie had gone off in search of food. Behind her, Moxy produced a circular piece of tin which he banged on repeatedly, chanting. It was now a quarter to three and he had been going since ten that morning. Louie returned with a couple of cold sausage rolls. He ate three and three quarters of them, offering Jenna a quarter. That was just about how their relationship was divided out, Jenna thought. There was a chill wind blowing round the ground. She fished her waterproof out of the bag.

'Do you want yours, Louie?' she asked.

The predicted rain was starting to fall.

'No thanks,' he replied, sinking his hands deep into the pocket of his hoodie.

'You not cold?'

'Nah,' he replied.

The game started. The players kicked the ball to each other while the spectators ooohed and oomphed.

'Is this what League Two football looks like?' she asked, surprised by how amateurish it all seemed. Okay, so she hadn't expected World Cup level football. But they were like a group of schoolboys kicking a ball around a desolate field behind a housing estate somewhere.

She took out her phone and scrolled through Twitter, Instagram, Facebook, the news. On the weather app, big black clouds hung threateningly over Barrow.

'You not watching the game?' Louie asked. She put her phone away.

A ball went off the pitch and everyone shouted, 'Corner!'

They waited anxiously, but no goal was scored.

She noticed a woman in her early twenties in the next row along. Moxy had spotted her too, and he went over to her with his little band. She had long black hair, plaited. Classy makeup for the joint she found herself in. A nice coat.

'Who's she?'

'WAG, innit,' replied Louie.

'WAG? Fuck sake, no.' Jenna laughed. 'Do you get WAGs at this level?'

Moxy was asking her all the questions Jenna herself wanted to know. She was here to watch Muldoon, yes, American, she was studying for an MBA and had a semester on an exchange programme at the London School of Economics. She met Muldoon in a nightclub.

'What's she doing here?' Jenna asked.

'She's Muldoon's girlfriend.'

'I understand that, but I mean, an MBA? She isn't exactly following the money.' Jenna sneered. 'How much do they get paid?'

Louis shrugged. 'Just watch the game.'

'I'm watching,' she said.

'Not really.'

'At least I'm here.'

Suddenly Barrow scored. The Barrow fans cheered and shouted.

'My own analysis here,' said Jenna, 'and I'll readily admit I know nothing about football, is that Barrow are not very good, but that Town are shit and have no chance of scoring.'

'They've only just got promoted,' Louie laughed. 'Give them a chance.'

'They're heading to demotion.'

'Relegation.'

Moxy tried to rally the Town fans with more drumming and chanting. 'Mighty, mighty Town!' And every time a Barrow player made some kind of error, he yelled, 'You're shit, and you know you are!'

'Why do you even like this?' Jenna asked.

'What do you mean?'

'The shouting and all that. Do you feel you belong to this crowd?'

'It's fun.'

'This?' she asked, incredulous.

'Lads, innit.'

The game finished 1-0 to Barrow.

'What a load of rubbish,' she said as they exited the ground and waved goodbye to Jason and Moxy. She got out her phone and used Google Maps to orient them to the hotel. You could smell the sea, and in an inlet there were some geese which made her excited for the nature reserve now they'd done Louie's part of the day.

By the time they reached the hotel it was raining steadily. They waited to check in while two men with a set of golf clubs were given their keys.

When it was their turn, Jenna asked about the nature reserve. The receptionist showed her a map and told her where to get the bus from the reserve. They'd be able to walk back to the pub she'd booked for dinner.

'Have you got some waterproofs?' the receptionist asked. 'The weather is about to turn nasty.'

In the room, they'd been given one double bed rather than two singles. Louie spread himself out on it like some giant mutant starfish.

'Where are you sleeping?' he asked, laughing.

'Don't get too comfortable. We're going out!'

'It's raining!'

Jenna looked outside to the alleyway below the window. The rain was pouring down now, but she was determined to go.

'That's why we brought our coats! Come on! Shift yourself!'

She opened his backpack to look for his coat.

'Where's your coat?'

'I dunno!'

She opened her own backpack. It wasn't there either. She poured the contents of Louie's backpack out on the bed. Not there.

'Louie,' she said, 'how could you do that? You left it at home so we wouldn't have to go to the nature reserve!'

'I didn't know it was going to rain.'

'Oh Louie! I could bloody kill you!'

'At least I'm here!'

Seeing the look on her face, he sighed. 'We can go anyway.'

But the rain was falling in torrents, puddles forming in the alleyway.

'Your sweatshirt would be soaked through in minutes.'

'Just come and lie down here, Jenna, have a little rest.'

With a sigh, she lay down and, as she had sat on the bus, put one foot on the floor, holding on. Only now she was seething. She tried to console herself, thinking that what he was, was typical.

'What are we going to do?' Louie asked.

'Just lie here 'til it's time to go to the pub.'

'Fair enough. Can I have a pint at the pub?'

He got up off the bed and found a charger, plugged his phone in, swiped through it until he found a football match, then lay his head on the pillow and started to watch it. Jenna tried to block out the annoying commentary. She'd even prefer a repeat of the camping weekend that time Louie had bought an Ouija board, and they spent the night screaming and scaring each other hysterical until that sensitive boy was sick.

When it was time, she asked the receptionist to get them a taxi to the pub. It drove them over the sea to Walney Island. She peered out of the misted taxi windows. This was all she would see of it. The taxi dropped them at the pub. The rain was coming down in sheets. In the short dash inside the pub, they were both soaked.

At the bar she ordered half a lager and a gin and tonic.

'Who is the lager for?' asked the barman.

'My son.'

'Is he over 18?'

Jenna nodded. 'Ahmmmm.'

'Is that him over there?' he asked, nodding to the table where Louie sat looking clean cut and youthful.

'Yes.'

'Does he have any ID?'

Jennie looked at the barman and then at Louie who, legs sprawled across the rug in front of the fire, his phone balanced in the folds of his wet hoodie, was watching Jenna warily.

'He's 6'1,' she said.

'That doesn't prove his age.'

'We're only here for the night; we didn't think to bring ID.'

'Lots of lads have it on their phones these days.'

'Are you accusing me of lying?' Jenna asked, combative.

'I can't serve him if he's underage.'

'It's only a lager for f—' she started to say, but then hesitated because to escalate could end up with a long walk back to the mainland in the pouring rain.

Just then the burly, bearded landlord came from the other side of the bar. This might be it. The endgame.

'The barrel needs changing,' he said to the barman.

The barman set down the glass and walked towards the cellar steps. 'Now, love, what can I get you?'

'Half a lager,' she said. 'And a coke for my son, here,' nodding to Louie.

He poured the lager, then uncapped a bottle of coke. He took his time about it. Jenna wanted him to hurry, to get away from the bar before the barman returned. She primed her card, ready to tap on his machine, then dashed the drinks over to Louie.

'Down that lager in one,' she said.

'You're so embarrassing. I'd've been happy with a coke. Why did you have to pick an argument with him?'

'He was getting on my nerves,' she said. 'But, really, the mood started with you.'

Louie looked slightly ashamed. 'Even with coats, we'd've got soaked.'

She pushed the drink over to him. 'Don't let that barman see you or we'll be kicked out.'

'What about your drink?'

'I'll get one when that lager's finished,' she said, taking a pack of cards from her bag. 'Fancy a game of rummy?'

She shuffled the cards and dealt them.

When Louie emptied his glass, she swopped the bottle of coke for the empty lager glass, which sat in front of her now, waiting for the barman to collect it.

She went to the bar and ordered some food and a large G&T for herself. When she got back to the table, she saw Louie was looking at her hand.

'For God's sake, Louie!' she said, packing away the cards.

When the food arrived, Louie ate his chips with his fingers, dipping them in a mound of ketchup he squeezed out of a plastic bottle, all the while watching his phone.

It was funny how you could give birth to someone you regarded now as you would an alien, she thought as she watched him. And though the alien child was born from you, he felt the same about you. She thought of them as two worlds colliding.

'Man City won. 2-0. Chenchenko got sent off—'

'Oh,' she said.

'—in the last minute for a high tackle.' He wiped his chawn fingernails on the soaking hoodie. 'Why are you looking at me like that?'

'I was thinking that if this was a first date, there wouldn't be a second one.'

'Same,' he snapped.

The pub door opened and the golfers from the hotel tumbled inside, letting in cold, rainy air, the evening dark already. Summer was ending in Barrow-in-Furness. She thought of motherhood as having seasons. The winter of the baby years, the child's banshee wailing, hunger or teething, while she walked around in the darkness, like some demented maiden in a high tower. Then the renewed hope of spring when they went to school. And early summer when they blossomed into youth, and you could almost relate as human beings. The family culture that developed gave you a sense of belonging. And now summer was ending, late August, and before long, he'd be off, his time with her done and she'd be left to darkening autumn evenings alone. She felt tears prick her eyes. It must be the gin.

'Mum!' she heard Louie say. 'What's going on?'

She sniffed and wiped her eyes. 'Oh, nothing!' she said. 'I was just thinking about those cockle pickers.'

'Don't think about them! I was talking to you about Man City. But then your eyes... It's so embarrassing!'

'I heard you,' she said. 'Chenchenko got sent off.'

'Do you even know what team he plays for?'

'Does it matter?'

Louie sighed. 'We shoulda just got the bus back with the others.'

'I couldn't take another three hours of that.'

But it wasn't just the bus. She wanted the night with him here in the pub before it was his mates in the pub. She wanted the reassuring sound of his breathing in the bed beside her even if she was forced to lie on one edge of it. Even here she was showing him the ropes of adulthood the way she'd taught him everything else. But one day he'd use those ropes to climb over a wall and make his escape. She dreaded the day when he broke free. Whereas he was just biding his time.

'I'll get us a taxi,' she said.

She returned a few minutes later.

'Gonna be half an hour for the taxi,' she told Louie, who sighed and returned to his phone.

She took a notebook out of her bag and started to write a list of everything he needed before the blessed day when he went back to school.

'What you doing?'

'Writing.'

'What?'

'A poem,' she lied, to exact a morsel of revenge.

'What about?'

'Today.'

'What is there to say?' he asked, his voice ragged, in a sort of teenage despair. 'It's just a game of football...'

He watched her write a few words.

'What's it called?'

'Summer is ending in Barrow-in-Furness.'

He rolled his eyes so far back she thought they'd be lost forever.

'I'll read it to you at bedtime if you like.'

'Perfect end to a perfect day.'

'It might be good.'

'I don't think it will be,' Louie declared.

'Why not?' she asked.

'How could it be? It's a poem,' he said, 'innit.'

SUN BUN

My mother keeps giving me pots of jam.

They have strange names like *Love,*
Full of Goodness, and *This Will Make You Feel Better.*

One was even called
You Need a Bit of Sweetness to Give You Strength.

I protest and tell her they are too sweet, that I prefer
jam less boiled, with less sugar.

She mixes everything from the garden
with the power of the sun. No longer calls me

Son Bun in front of the boys nor stitches
my homework poems together. Once said

I let you go a long time ago as I strained to be free,
her understanding like the quiet of a country stream.

If you meet her, your name is on a candle linking fire to the creator,
the Greeks called him Helios, I call her mum.

My mother keeps giving me pots of jam.

DIARMUID CAWLEY

ROYALTY

It was worth it, Da. I got locked and coronated. And sang songs to the snotty cows, called them darling and remembered

how I'd snoozed against their warm sides, fingers cramping in the pre-dawn, consoled by the hiss and ring of a filling bucket.

And that first time, looking out over the harrowed fields at a drear day, thinking they'd be gone for hours, not knowing the drink'd floor me,

my thoughts lurched then danced and soon I ruled over every blooming thing and all I said made penetrating sense,

though only the cows would hear it, this time. And then, I was unconquerably tired and he was back from the funeral,

full of fury that the bottle he'd been craving was empty and his scut of son with the clever mouth had done it.

I'd watched him for years drink himself legendary then tumble into mumbling rage. I know I'm meant to bemoan the fists

but it's the beaming glory of his face that remains, the power in him that the days' defeats couldn't overwhelm.

That's what I was after, sitting on the cold stone, slurry round my feet, tasting the bite and burn of it for the first time. Thinking, I can be a king too.

PHIL KINGSTON

JOURNEY IN HEAVY SNOW

You made the journey through snow
in the blue Renault.
Mother at the window all day,
a frozen statue

swaying closer to the frozen fir trees,
her hands dead swallows
on the window panes.
I thought she would fall through

and be a log covered in snow,
dotted with twiggy prints of robin-feet,
apron stiff with frost,
rusty-chimes of clothes line

heard inside all day, slow clock-ticks.
She always watched the robin
when she peeled turnips.
You have her face,

fear of the outside
double-stitched in both your eyes.
You both like skirts with darts at the waist,
very similar,

very difficult to get through winter,
to carry you through the snow.

EIBHLÍS CARCIONE

122

UISCÍ BEO

Tá aibhneacha baininscneach.
Farraigí? Mná uaisle.
Aigéin? Bandéithe maorga móra.
Iad uilig ag suaitheadh,
Ag síorathrú,
An saol mór ag tarraingt orthu.
Páistí ar a dtránna agus ar a mbruacha,
Foghlaithe ar bharr a dtonnta,
Ollphéisteanna i bhfolach sna duibheagáin thíos.
Caithníní siocaithe sneachta sa gheimhreadh, deora beaga crua.
Ag cur de dhíon is de dheora san earrach, deora boga mánla.
Gach braon ag titim ar an chré,
Ag sileadh is ag tochailt síos
Chuig uiscí eile, ag triall ar
A mbealach féin
Sa tsaol.

RÉALTÁN NÍ LEANNÁIN

BEITHÍOCH

SEOSAMH Ó FÁTHARTA

Facthas ar dtús í ag spaisteoireacht thar mhullach Sliabh Gleann Eidhneach. Iascairí ar an chuan a d'aimsigh í, meall beag ghlais i bhfad i gcéin ag triail ar buaic na spéire. Ach ba dhoiligh an beithíoch a dhéanamh amach i gclapsholas trom an fhómhair. Ar dtús, de réir a gcuid súl, mheas siad gur bodóg a bhí ann, bodóg leathan ag crapadh siar ar éigin, eireaball fada ardaithe chuig na réalta, crochta go himníoch seans, amhail chreach truamhéalaí éigin sainnithe idir fál is díog, dhá shúil dírithe ar dhrannadh mictíre na sean Fhódla a bhí tar éis teacht sna cosa in airde transa na ngort.

Ach i dtrácht na haimsire tugadh an amhairc chun grinnis. Ní raibh sé thar an gcoitiantacht do mhuintir an Bhoirinn an beithíoch a fheiceáil sna gclochair i gcoim na tsléibhe, nó ag seasamh ar chairn clocha ar a mharana amhail dealbh ársa, ag mungailt ar thaibhrimh choimhthíocha. Tháinig tuairiscí uathu siúd a tháinig ina ngaobhar. Labhair siad faoina gcraiceann righin rocach, macasamhail d'aolchloch ghágach na gnoc neamhthorthúil; na súile beaga bioracha a dhearbhaigh an intleacht is cruinneas cuimhne agus leis sin ámh, a chumha; cheithre chos thamhanta basach a chuir an talamh ag creathadh le teann a choiscéime; an trunc eireaballach, a chuireadh madraí na dúiche ar báiní nuair a mhúsclaíodh solas báiteach na gealaí a gháir stoic uaigneach.

Céard a thug ann í? Cá bhfios. Dála gach rud eile, níl againn ach tuairimíocht is barúlacha. An uair deiridh a bhfacthas í bhí sí á níochán féin i gclais srutha a shil isteach go sáile an chuain. Ansin d'imigh sí as amharc. Is dóigh gur éag sí. Deirtear go raibh sí míchothaithe. Deir eile gurbh í an sioc a chuir deireadh léi. Níor thángadar ar aon conablach ná cnámh. Ina honóir, thóg na daoine leacht gharbh d'aolchloch scaoilte na dúiche ar mhullach Sliabh Gleann Eidhneach, a dheilbhigh siad ina cruth. Deirtear ar oícheanta stoirmiúila nuair a shéideann na gaoithe láidre aduaidh thríd scoilteachaí idir na clocha, go gcloistear gáir stoic an bheithígh chéanna ag baint macalla as na cnoic is na gleannta.

OBSESSED WITH ANTLERS

Even snug in his mother's womb, he can feel them growing,
Victoriana rebooted for Instagram —
an embryonic Monarch of the Glen,
his fabulous headgear iconic on every shelf
of the gift shop, glossy on calendars, craggy in bronze,
his future a frenzied series of You Tube clips,
his bellowing disrupting tourists' sleep
all autumn long, the weight of all that roaring
dragging his body forward into a pose
where he has to lock antlers with some random male —
but what if he doesn't want to be iconic?
What if he only wants one hind, or none?
What if he wants to duck out of the whole agenda?

We saw them once at dusk: three young, shy deer
materializing out of the grey-brown bog,
stepping through willow scrub and clumps of reeds,
keeping a wary eye on us as they grazed,
lifting their heads – three perfect triangles
from delicate nose to ears flared wide, alert.
These ones were not souvenir material.
They disappeared before we could grab our phones
for photos to prove they were ever really there:
two hinds, unobtrusive, soft and brown as sparrows,
the third, no bigger, indistinguishable,
except that above his startled eyes were stumps
of velvet-covered horn the length of my thumb,
seeming from a distance barely thicker
than a blade of marsh grass teased by the summer wind.

JANET SHEPPERSON

MIDSUMMER

I think of the dark readying its slow return
and wait to feel the tilt of the earth
shift. Here at the vernal equinox
I want to race beyond the solstice.
Last June, late, I scanned the hills
looking for bonfires on St John's Eve.
Tongues blazed across Seanadh Phéistín
bog where the dark remained
distant as twilight wasn't finished
with the sea. If it weren't for that
western glow I could've read the book
of the sky, the stories in the stars.
What comfort does daylight carry?
Wrap me here in night.

JAMIE O'HALLORAN

BOG BODY

Slumped over IKEA desk, dusk delayed since time
slipped back and morning darkened, having just
returned from the garden, tying light ropes around
hollow trees to serenade starlight, trying to avoid
the knot of noose, I open a book to catch Fernando
Pessoa bleeding over The Book of Cesario Verde.

I sing that same sorrow! Reduced to countryman,
returned to mud of the country and the man — so far
from the cities where he burnt his skin on freedom.
I write of other houses for fear I'll forget where I laid,
sketch shadows already disappearing from streets
I once identified by scent, where I once discovered
what it was like to find your way out of being lost.

One writes and no one reads, till he dies. The other —
leaning, reading, bleeding. We are only as devious
as our smiles are wide, feeling pressed between
the beauty of a flower indoors and the snap of a stem
from its root. Bound between page and peat,
I walk these fields, bleeding for the smell of a city.

DAMIEN DONNELLY

DÓCHAS

Ardú croí
Neartú brí
Buanú meanman
Díobairt bróin
Athbheochan misnigh
Síol an dóchais
Faoiseamh aigne
Ag síneadh romhainn.

Spioraid dúisithe
Fuinneamh dírithe
Ar dhearfacht smaointe
`S ar choráiste ár ndaoine
Spréach ag speachadh as luaithe an donais
`S aoibhneas i ndán dúinne
A chreideann sa tseoid.

Gruaimeacht scaipithe
Ag ráitisí dearfa
An griothal go doicheallach
Ag pléascadh mar neascóid
Scaoil chugainn go héadrom
Coiscéimeanna bríomhara
an dóchais ag rince
`S á cheilliúradh le ceol.

Suaimhneas intinne
Buanú muiníne
`S iomar na haimléise

I bhfad ón ár gcuimhne
Solas ar lasadh
I ndoircheacht na hoíche
Coinneal an dóchais
Ag soilsiú an róid.

EIBHLÍN UÍ IARLAITHE

THE COTTAGE

KEVIN MACALAN

I

The cold bit through Oscar's work gloves as he grasped the corrugated iron and wrenched aside the hanging door. It squealed in protest, the rusted wheels it hung from dragging across the runner, not rolling as they would have a lifetime before. Paint remained only in places, some flaking off the dinted corrugations, some dull and faded, but though mostly grey or rusted, the rattling tin curtain still lived up to the notion of a green door. Once open, it waved in the wind, clanging against the whitewashed stone walls of the single story shed until Oscar jammed it in place with the broken masonry block that had previously wedged it shut.

This was his now. The five degrees lost living halfway up the mountain might take some getting used to, but the proceeds from the sale of his father's cosy coastal cottage when split with his sister had afforded him this home unencumbered, and unencumbered was the only way a man with his income and his history could live. Firing up the oil burner would certainly help. A hole in the roof gaped above his head and whistling gusts rattled through the rotting timbers. 'That'll need fixing,' thought Oscar, glancing around, and having the same thought a dozen times over.

Though the season boasted spring, Oscar's breath condensed into ghostly mists which hung before him as his eyes accommodated to the gloom and took in the room. A vast green oil storage tank propped up on four piles of concrete blocks dominated the space which smelled of damp and soil, kerosene and desertion. He leant into the tank and lifted one end, the sloosh showed there was some fuel at home, the weight suggested not much.

In the far corner the oil burner, a Popular 90, sat thickly coated in brick dust and cobwebs. To the left of that a Welsh dresser standing five feet tall had three ornately fashioned wooden shelves fronting a knotted pine tongue-and-groove backboard above twin drawers and door-fronted cabinets. A quality piece of furniture, one cupboard had only half a door, one drawer had no front, the tongue-and-groove was dissembling. The dresser was here to die. It lay in state between the Popular 90 to its right, and an ancient wooden pallet, the sort used for handling loads with a forklift, to its left. The pallet was up-ended and propped against the wall. Between the pallet and the wall three aged raw wood timber planks festooned in cobwebs and caked in dust appeared to defy gravity and stand to regimental attention. Oscar noted them but made a path toward his quarry: the Popular 90.

II

With heat coursing through pipes and radiators, the cottage returned to life. It breathed. Oscar heard its old joints crack as they stretched. And when he stepped in from outside, stooping through the tiny front door directly into the one living room, he felt warmed. Along the back wall, a staircase led up to two bedrooms, access to the second being through the first. There was also a door into the kitchen, an obvious later addition. In the kitchen a door had been knocked through into part of the adjoining shed, the shed that housed the oil burner, except the part accessed via the kitchen had been walled off and fitted out as a bathroom. The only two chairs in the lounge faced the open fireplace, which, though modestly sized, had an impressive oak surround. One of these chairs, a high-backed dark wood rocker with well-worn carved arms, had a faded embroidered cushion in the seat secured at each corner by plaited silken cords. The other, a small Queen Anne with stained Damask upholstery, had wooden feet which seemed to have been gnawed by an animal. Oscar was pleased, but the kerosene was soon exhausted.

He set a fire and watched the logs ripple with dancing flames. He sat in the small Queen Anne. Firewood crackled, and the warmth built beneath the room's low ceiling. The rocking chair moved perceptibly. Oscar felt at home, but at somebody else's home. It was dusk, and the only light inside the cottage came from the fire.

'What should I call you?' he asked gently. 'Miss Ryan? Or can I call you Brigid?' A wintry wind still clamoured outside and a gust slipped beneath the door mewing like a stray and flickering the fire.

'Call me what you will,' Oliver heard.

'Brigid then.'

'I haven't moved far.'

'I know. Just to the churchyard on the other side of the boreen.'

The draught beneath the door moaned. 'That'll need fixing,' thought Oscar.

III

With an order of kerosene due, Oscar set about clearing a path for the delivery. His first week in the cottage was ending as it had begun, dragging aside the green corrugated door that shielded the oil burner room from the Comeraghs. The roller wheels that suspended the door rotated and rumbled along the runner, several applications of WD40 having eased their protests. The wind, still cold, fidgeted beneath a brilliant cloudless sky, and Oscar brought the masonry block doorstop heavily against the open door to pin it against the shed.

Across the way, the Catholic church of St. Médard of Picardy grew from the hill to shelter headstones, mountain ash, and hawthorn trees, and Oscar saw Brigid leaning on the churchyard wall not forty paces from the cottage. So short that only her face and shoulders rose above the drystone boundary. She rested her head on interlocked hands and looked out on the world with idle eyes. Oscar let her be and went inside.

The burner room, more brightly lit, revealed the detail of its squalor. Rusted hand tools, anonymous and unobvious in their application, lay on every surface beneath a dressing of dust as coarse as sand. Oscar grabbed a tin pail and gathered several of the smaller items together. He shifted an iron wheel that lay on its back in the middle of the floor within the shredded remains of a pneumatic tyre by wheeling it to one side, and he pulled the up-ended pallet away from the wall. The regimentally upright timbers behind remained regimentally upright, being strapped together by wooden struts and held in place by hinges. They were a door.

IV

Late spring the winter abated, but Oscar, who had been gifted a tractor bucket of firewood as a welcome from a neighbour, kept a fire in the grate most nights. He had acquired a standard lamp and draped a rugged blanket over the Queen Anne where he would sit and read late, sometimes waking to dying embers with the rug wrapped around his legs against the first-light cold of another mountain morning.

'Did you cover me up like that?' Oscar asked of Brigid.

'Ye haven't the sense ye were born with,' he heard the reproval in her tone.

'My own father couldn't have said it better.'

'And where is he?'

'He's with you.'

Oscar rekindled the fire and boiled the kettle to make tea. He made two cups from the one bag, set Brigid's down on the hearth before the rocking chair, and cradled his own to warm his hands as he returned to sit and take stock.

'Why are ye here?'

'Peace, I think.' Oscar took a breath. 'I was away when my father died. I'd been away for several years, and they wouldn't give me day release for the funeral.'

'Ah...'

Oscar sensed a loss of sympathy. 'Don't be like that,' he urged.

'There'll be no judgement here. We all need somewhere to be. We all deserve peace.'

V

The room behind the raw timber door swallowed light into a velvet darkness. It was a foreboding secret of a place. Oscar pushed against the door's rough surface; the hinges had been unused for so long they behaved like springs coiled against opening. Eventually they were overcome and spilled the door into the musty void. Oscar waited and listened, expecting to hear scurrying, but not a sound met his ears. His eyes blinded by the absorbent dark, his only sense of the room was the eery chill on his face and the heavy air in his nostrils. It took the beam of a flashlight to dispel the black. With its help, Oscar slowly realised this was only half a room, and what an elegant room the whole one must have been. Wallpapered walls supported an architrave ceiling. A fireplace looked lost positioned to one side of the wall behind the door, and ornate plaster cornices on the ceiling framed only three of the walls. The fourth was marine ply, and Oscar realised only now that he was standing outside his bathroom. He'd never considered the measurements as being off, but the footprint of the cottage had obviously been extended into the farm shed to provide extra this living space, which later was divided into two to create the luxury of a bathroom. This parlour sacrificed on the altar of progress had probably been shut off for decades. The rough timber door an afterthought, crudely knocked through the wall to allow access that was never used. Oscar's boots left footprints like Armstong's on the moon. The wallpaper came away in sheets, bringing with it plaster from the walls. In places it seemed only cobwebs held the room together, but before leaving, Oscar vowed to return this half place to half its former glory.

VI

Sat in the Queen Anne under a cone of light from the standard lamp, Oscar was finding the constant rocking of Brigid's chair disturbing. Two months had passed and a June was promised that would bring warmer weather, but still he had a fire in the grate, burning the wood his neighbour gave him for allowing two ponies to graze on the cottage's acre. The book on his knee was filled with mostly blank pages. He wrote now, rather than read, and hearing Brigid as he could was not helping his focus.

'Whatever the weather on St. Médard's day, expect the same for forty more.'

'Funny you should say that Brigid,' Oscar set down his book with a hint of irritation. 'I was just writing about that, June 8th.' He hesitated. 'Look Brigid, I think it's time. I have something to show you. Meet me in the shed.'

Without waiting to gauge Brigid's response he picked up her chair and followed her out of the cottage.

The freshly painted green corrugated door slid aside smoothly. Oscar carried in Brigid's chair. He knew she was impressed by the tidy oil burner room. A clinical white light, triggered by a motion-sensor, illuminated the dust-free space. Canopied by a solid roof, the shed had an integrity previously missing. The odour of desertion had gone, though a hint of kerosene remained. Also gone was the broken dresser and the random pallet and trailer wheel. The most striking difference was the new wooden door, finished in high-gloss white paint and complete with door furnishings, that graced the wall to the left of the sparkling Popular 90.

Oscar lifted the latch and gently swung the door open. He waited a beat to let Brigid ahead of him, then followed with her chair. The room gleamed. Magnolia walls contrasted a pristine white ceiling with crisp painted cornices and a crystal lampshade that Oscar had found while tidying the shed. The firebox had been boarded up above the hearth, but painted flames devoured painted logs and the mantel shelf bore trinkets and knick-knacks recovered from the cottage. Oscar set down Brigid's chair in front of the fire. Behind the chair, the Welsh dresser with a restored backboard, new cabinet door, and drawer front took pride of place in this half-seen room. Brigid's room.

'We all need somewhere to be. We all deserve peace,' he said. 'I'll leave the door on the latch.'

Before leaving, Oscar cast his eye around the room. A framed photograph he'd found of Brigid, younger, outside the cottage cradling a lamb, now stood centrally on the middle dresser shelf.

'Fierce independent and house proud', the neighbour had described her.

'Fixed it,' thought Oscar.

FAOILEOIR SPÉIRE

}}>
Beirim
mo chuid fola
is mo chuid fulaingthe
suas go dtí na hairde ar eití
os cionn cnoic atá bán le sneachta
balbh ag an áilleacht go cró mo bhoilg   }>
dall ar an saol daonna
ar an dochar déanta
ar an gcath laethúil.   ....
Cith chalóga sneachta
anuas orm, rud a ghreamaíonn dóchas   }>
ina lándúiseacht istigh im' chroí
go dtí go gcím tríd an mbán
na braonacha dearga
is tuirlingím scun
scan, féachaint
bhfuil aon ní
fágtha
slán.
}>

CEAITÍ NÍ BHEILDIÚIN

SIX SIGMA ON THE GLENHEST ROAD

*Wait times prevent smooth flow and
point to process constraints*
—IBM Redguide

At the top of the lane I come across Liam Óg replacing saplings lopped by an overzealous Council crew. He secretes them now at intervals along the hedgerow, enjoying the vision of a future looming. *They think we want to get there faster*, he says. *But that was never what this road was about.*

People used to drop in all the time. Or just knock on the window to wave. Now it is all cars and rushing about hither thither and yon. Minnie Chambers stirs her tea, laughing with us about the so-much-time passed, but our very presence (and that of the new furniture set she has bought in readiness for her wake) has given us all pause.

*'Twas about faces, chat —
the Yew Cottage kettle
is already on*

Next door, Liam plants oaks
on the hedged bend we share —
riposte to any scythe.

FIN KEEGAN

EAGLE

for Eibhear Walshe

Only here and there does the old roadway
Show itself through the overwhelming bog.
Now and then centuries of disuse relent

And allow hollowed-out passages, or stone
Foundations lift themselves out of the heather.
A broken line, barely visible on the old map

Goes astray in a tangle of roots, snagging itself
On rusted barbed wire fences before sinking
From sight as surely as it sank from memory.

Only on the higher ground, where the wind
Has flayed bare the shoulders of Mullach Beag,
Does the road again assert its sinewy strength.

We have walked up through ruined settlements
Where generations had scraped out survival
Before the lakeside road below us was built.

Their hard-won houses and walls have long
Faded to anonymous rectangles on old maps.
Now, high up, as we approach Cnoc an Fhiolair,

Huge wings soar from their own extinct name
Over deserted townlands, like some descendant
Of emigrants getting to know the old territories.

Moving too fast for binoculars, that restored
Presence glides past, losing itself in clouds.
We turn again, resume tracing the old road.

PADDY BUSHE

Cnoc an Fhiolair: Eagle Hill

SITE NOTICE: CHARLO STREET

'What is not injurious to the city does not injure the citizens either. On the occasion of every imagination that you have been injured, apply this canon: 'If the city is not injured by this neither am I injured. But if the city is injured you must not be angry, only point out to him who injured the city what he has failed to see.'
— Marcus Aurelius, Meditations (trans. A.S.L. Farquharson, 1944).

Heading into work one of the days, I amble down
past the Charlo Street flats, where breeze blocks,
prefabs and chrome, wind-worn hoarding
    cordon off the sledgehammer knocks
    while a hard-hatted foreman
sparks up a rollie before inking X's and Y's
    on his clipboard. The flats, ripe for demolition,
    are to be bulldozed and a newer, glossier edifice
raised in place, with past tenants not alerted.
    Were I to nick a keepsake from the detritus,
    can I hope for a better standard of living?
And sure, the days of plenty and profit are back,
    but is now really the time for thanksgiving?

Just as before, a thicket of cranes snag the skyline,
iron jibs grab at cloud or star, as the wind's high grip
rattles through the bony lattice and chain-
    sling as they slowly swivel to lift
    granite slabs to the roof.
At a temporary bus-stop, I take screenshots of the site,
    levelled as if by earthquake or war,
    dust-sprays gasping amid clearance.
This is a hard-hat area, waspy drill-rasp driving

each bolted screw into place, gloved and harnessed
scaffolders drudging above potholed tarmac.
And Death walks among them always, a rumble of certainty
    in its step. They waste no time on sorrow or awe

for the flats and their damaged goods. Cement mixers
pour grey sludge through caked chutes,
a JCB lies toppled on its side, a grubby sphinx
    muck-caked and waiting. In an hour,
    ice pellets will plummet, knifing the air, rhythmical
as drill-beats, echo across the site. Excavators lurch over
    to chomp down infrastructural lumps and steel
    bracing dismantled, all the wiring torn by the roots,
compressed into dust. Green netting shrouds the links
    and the ladders are fixed in propped positions
    yet not a single storey contains a soul to soar
aloft to hallowed gates, for careworn morticians,
    disposing of a deadweight carcass, to adore.

Monoliths of stylised brick, I've seen more and more
of them sprout up, slow but sure as sunrise,
skyline-usurpers, their banners marked
    with company logos and bashed by breeze.
    I keep on walking, pressed now for time,
hands scalded by a Costa cup and unremarked
    by the foreman, away from the site perimeter
    to where traffic lights bleep from green
to red, and headlamps swarm to Harcourt
    as if joining in a pitiless, ultra-modern raid.
    The screenshots are stored away in my phone
and I pick up the pace. But I'm afraid,
    for what future is being reaped, there and then?

DANIEL WADE

VERY OFTEN TRUE

SUE HANN

The metal of the door handle is cool in my clammy hands, and I pause a second to calm myself before I twist it open. I take a breath, scrunching my toes slightly—my new shoes pinch, my feet more accustomed to the canvas sloppiness of Converse trainers. This is my first proper job since graduating from college with an undergraduate degree in Psychology. I have spent four years ordering books from deep in the stacks of the library, taking notes assiduously, learning how to structure an academic essay and writing up reports. Today, for the first time, I will be working with a human. I am a research assistant and I have finished my on-the-job training, I have been through the interview protocol, familiarised myself with the questionnaires, how they are scored, how they are phrased. This is the first interview that I'm doing by myself.

As I open the door into the reception area, there is a man waiting for me. My participant. Ignoring the row of empty chairs, he is on his feet, looking out of the window, hands clasped behind his back, moving slightly, rocking from foot-to-foot.

I am aware of my appearance and feel self-conscious that I look like a child in the dress-up clothes of an adult. Being small in stature makes me look younger than my 22 years, something I feel hinders my being taken seriously. My new shirt feels sweaty around the armpits already, and it rubs against the waistband of my skirt as we walk the short steps to the interview room.

He hesitates in the doorway as I gesture to the chair, eyeing up the stack of papers I have laid out on the table. Perhaps the official look of the forms makes it real for him, and there is a split second as he stands on the threshold where I think that he might not come in. That he might turn on his heel, walk back down the corridor, out to the lobby, walk smartly down the two flights of stairs—not bothering to wait for the lift—and out into the concrete safety of the campus car park.

But he does come in. I allow my lungs free rein again and smile and try to put him at ease. I introduce myself.

'How are you?' he says in response. Because what does one say in a situation like this? Where a total stranger, young enough to be your daughter, will ask you about things that you have never allowed to rise up from the bile of your belly and leave your mouth.

'Fine, thank you,' I say, but I do not return his question because that question is the one I am here to find answers to over the next few hours. I talk instead about the weather, the traffic, small familiar things, the last bit of safe ground that he will know for the rest of the morning.

As he sips from the white plastic cup of filtered water that I will refill for him many times over the course of the interview, I tell him about my role, that I am part of a team of interviewers on this project, that I will be asking him lots of questions, and later I will complete the scoring and results and submit them back to the project team for analysis.

He fiddles with the rounded lip of the cup as I finish my rehearsed speech. His hands are rough and the cuticles are creeping up his nail, thick bands of skin.

And this is how we begin.

Industrial schools were set up in Ireland in the second half of the 1800's by the State and run by religious orders to care for children who were orphaned or children who were in trouble with the law. Over the next few decades, these schools would grow in size and number.

The national scandal of the scale of child abuse in Irish institutions hit when I was a teenager. A documentary series in the late 1990's broke open the silence surrounding industrial schools. The reality of these institutions was exposed—they were more like prisons than schools. Children could be sent there through the magistrates' court for crimes sometimes very minor, or if their families could not look after them, for whatever reason; death, poverty, being unwed. Abuse was endemic; neglect, physical, emotional, and sexual abuse. The conditions were poor, there wasn't enough food, and often the food that was provided was inedible.

That the State knew about these horrific conditions was clear. The detail was there in the reports from inspection after inspection. One government report, in its neat typewritten script, noted that the cows on the farmland of the institution were better fed than the children.

The Taoiseach at the time made an apology on behalf of the State and ordered a judicial enquiry. In the self-entered way of teenagers, this tragedy felt far removed from me. A devastation only in print.

When I shuffle through my memories of my grandfather, there is little there. By the time I knew him—if I can say that I knew him at all—a series of strokes had left him partially paralysed. He walked with a cane, leaning heavily on it, shifting his weight to drag his bad leg along behind him. Not that he walked very far or very often, remaining usually in the small radius between his bedroom and his chair beside the fire.

I remember the formality to his dress: he always wore a collared shirt and trousers, with leather shoes. He had a shiny, bald pate, hearing aid nestled behind one ear, and was always clean-shaven.

As a child, the attraction of visiting my grandparents was mainly feeding the ducks that swam in the river next to the house, and a glass of TK red lemonade. The biscuit barrel in the shape of a dog's head sat on the cabinet, and we would eye it up, waiting for my grandmother to offer us one of the delights from the depths of the doggy's brain. It was usually a Kimberley's biscuit with its twin rows of pink marshmallow topped with flaked coconut on a soft biscuit base. My grandfather was a diabetic, so he would go without my grandmother's offerings.

The conversation passed between my mother, my grandmother, my aunt. My grandfather would be involved now and again.

'Would you like a cup of tea, Pat. I say, would you like a cup of tea, Pat?'

It was a running joke, my grandmother's habit of repeating everything she said twice. A habit that was probably long-learned as my grandfather was partially deaf, and his speech was poor since his strokes. To see him trying to speak was like watching a steam engine leave the station. I could see the energy building, the effort mounting as he would open his mouth and, vocal cords straining, face reddening with effort, he tried to summon sound from the back of his throat. With stutters and false starts, he would try to form a word, supplementing his speech with gestures with his good hand, pointing, asking for his sweetener perhaps, or for something else with his tea.

I don't know when I came to know that my grandfather was put in an industrial school as a young child. In the way of family folklore, it was known but not discussed, the details were hazy. I thought my grandfather spent a lot of his childhood there, until he was informally fostered out to a childless couple who owned farmland and were in need of labour. Years later, my aunt told me that he was put in the industrial school very young and spent a few years there before being fostered at around age 3.

That this account was so different from my own made-up memory surprised me. I had sentenced my grandfather to a much harsher childhood than he had. Instead real life gave him a lucky escape. Things could have been a lot worse.

The Old Woman, he used to call her, the woman who fostered him. And this detail saddens me, how impersonal it is, how removed. Disrespectful even.

Did he call her Mammy at aged 3? When did he switch to calling her the Old Woman? Did he call her by her first name face-to-face? What was her first name? After he got married and moved away, the Old Woman used to visit him, arriving on her pony and trap. My uncle and aunt, the oldest children, remember her visits. And it soothes me a little, knowing this. There was love there, it seems.

I don't remember the news stories of industrial school child abuse ever being spoken about at home in relation to my grandfather which now seems strange. If there were any conversations about it between my mother and her family when I got the job on this research project, I wasn't aware of them. Looking back now, I wonder if that silence was a form of denial or avoidance. Was this uncomfortable or distressing to my mother, to have this link with her father's early childhood experience? I don't recall her mentioning it. Nothing was said when I came home with a couple of appropriately sombre shirts and put on my most professional outfit for my first day on the job.

Pencil in one hand, I turn the page of my interview booklet, making sure not to miss any of the questions.

There are numerous questionnaires to complete, data to gather, some more difficult than others. I can feel my throat constrict slightly as I get closer to the trauma questionnaire. I am nervous about handling this sensitively, about getting it right, about causing the least amount of distress possible.

John, my interviewee, is flagging. I have been asking him questions for the past hour.

'Would you like a quick break, John? I can get you a fresh drink, you can stretch your legs'.

'No, no, sure I'm grand.'

He is not grand. We both know that. But I press on anyway.

'For the next part, I'm going to read you a series of statements, and ask you to choose between a set of response options, which are: never true, rarely true, sometimes true, often true, or very often true. I'll repeat these options to you after each question, as often as you need me to. Are you ready?'

He nods his assent.

'I knew that there was someone to take care of me and protect me. Never true, rarely true, sometimes true, often true, or very often true.'

He does not pause over this one, but gives a dry bark of a half-laugh instead. 'Never true,' he says.

I move on.

'I was punished with a belt, a board, a cord, or some other hard object.'

'Very often true,' he says.

'Someone tried to touch me in a sexual way or tried to make me touch them.'

There is a pause and he looks away, stares out the window at a branch of a tree that is swaying slightly in the breeze.

'Often true'.

He says it so quietly that I repeat it, wanting to make sure that I got it right. His lips thin and his mouth clamps shut, holding back more that will never be said. And in this moment, I am glad of the protection of these standardised questionnaires and screening tools with their forced choice answers. I move on to the next question.

I sat with so many men after John, men my father's age and older, in a stuffy office in a university with pencil hovering over the page.

'I've never spoken about it until today,' one man said.

Another brought his wife who held his hand as he tried not to cry. I looked down, giving him privacy.

And after they had gone, released back out into the day, I remember the heaviness left behind in the room, the urge to distract myself, to do something else quickly so that the heaviness wouldn't settle on my chest for good.

In some ways, the structure of the interviews protected me from the devil that lives in the detail. I came to know of how frequent these acts of. abuse were, but the specifics were left unsaid. It was hidden behind the boxes I ticked, the responses I circled, the questionnaires I scored. Each unspeakable misery, each decimation of the psyche, quantified into figures, added and totalled together.

It is twenty years since I took that job, and in truth there is much that I don't remember, much that I have blanked out. The corrosion of memory over time, partially, but also perhaps, not wanting to remember.

Now that I have grown into middle age and have my own child, I feel compelled to look at my extended family. It took me by surprise, this interest. I thought having a child would link me to the future, but instead it seemed to pull me back to the past. My own parents, my parents' parents. Wanting to understand how things went wrong in my family, to learn from mistakes of the past. An age-old wish, I suppose. Which is what got me thinking about my grandfather again. And my first job. I hadn't thought of that job, the stories I heard, the terrors hinted at, in a long, long time.

I do some research online on the industrial school that my grandfather was sent to; at maximum capacity, the school housed 825 children, and only closed in 1969, the year my mother turned 18.

I listen to radio interviews with men who were sent there, trying to imagine what my grandfather's early life was like. So many stories of lives ruined. Children from poor families sent there for minor infractions: stealing from a bread van, stealing rosary beads. All spoke of the extreme cruelty, horrendous abuse. The sexual abuse that happened in the confession box, the fondling that happened in the dormitories at night. One man talks about being beaten with a hurling stick over and over until his legs swelled up so much that they didn't fit his boots. His voice is a torrent of rage and hurt, still raw after all these years, and it is so very hard to listen to.

There are interviews also with family members. A son and daughter, grown now, talk about how their father never spoke of his childhood in an industrial school, never talked about the scar on his face that they assumed was caused by abuse he experienced there.

My grandfather did not speak of his biological parents, or of the industrial school. He kept his birth certificate in a strong box at home and kept the key hidden. The shame of growing up in care had to be locked away. He led a quiet life, cycling to work in a factory, having a pint at the weekend in his local pub, cooking a fry on a Sunday.

I think back now to my memories of sitting in my grandparent's front room, my brother and I, trying to be quiet and well-behaved, sat on the sofa, short legs sticking out over the edge. My grandfather in his armchair, holding a mug of his tea in his good hand. He was always silent, on the periphery of his own home, and I wonder what was going through his mind as he sat watching. Was he thinking of his child self at our age? What did he know of how he came into care? Did his mother die? Was he born to an unmarried mother and therefore placed in care like so many other babies in those times? There are so many questions that I have for him.

I look back on the questionnaires and screening tools now, all the questions I asked my participants, and I feel the weight of them, for my grandfather. *Did you feel loved? Were you made to feel important, were you looked out for? Did your family feel close? Was your family a source of strength?*

Most of what I know about my grandfather comes from the stories that my mother tells of her father being very strict, getting a wallop of his belt if she or her siblings came home late as teenagers.

Although I knew little of him really, the spectre of my grandfather's life still featured in the shadows of my own childhood. When I misbehaved as a small child, my mother would sometimes, in anger, threaten to send me away to boarding school. The shock of this was enough to stop whatever childish tantrum I was having.

Other times, she said it lightly, jokingly. 'Reform school is the only place for you,' she would say, and laugh trying to let me know, I suppose, that she wasn't serious. But it still confused me, because I never found it funny, the threat of being sent away. In my mind, boarding school and reform schools were the same thing, places you were sent to if you were bad. When I was older, I read the Enid Blyton books set in a girls' boarding school, and I realised that boarding schools are not meant to be places of punishment.

I wonder now whether my grandfather's time in an industrial school cast its shadow over my mother's childhood in ways that she could not express, and so it came, in some small measure, to cast a shadow over my own.

The past sits firmly in the present, nudging it on into the future. The pasts of our parents, and our parents' parents. And when that past is traumatic, the seeds of that trauma can get passed on too. What psychologists call intergenerational trauma. Whether trauma is passed down through learned behaviour or a mix of genes and behaviour, the debate continues.

Since my first job, I now know a lot more about the impact that a difficult childhood can have into adulthood. Large scale studies have tried to measure the impact. Researchers made a checklist of experiences: emotional abuse, physical abuse, sexual abuse, having a parent in prison, witnessing domestic violence... They followed children over decades and measured how their past impacted on their physical, emotional, and psychological health. They found that the more adverse experiences a child had from their checklist, the more likely they were to have health problems later in life including cardiac disease and diabetes (as in my grandfather's case), and the more likely they were to have mental health problems. He died of a heart attack in the end, my grandfather.

I think of the weight of things that he never talked about. His biological parents who lost their baby to an industrial school; being taken from his family at such a young age. The strong box and its shameful contents. I think of what his early life was like in the industrial school. John's words, and the words of all the other men I interviewed, fill the gaps of my grandfather's silence.

I look at my toddler daughter, her small, sturdy body, the four perfect dimples on the back of her knuckles, the fold of fat at her wrist, and the strands of DNA, twisted chains, like garlands, stretching down the generations. I think of the chromosomes dividing and splitting from these great-grandparents that no one knew, to my grandfather that I barely knew, to my mother, to me. Information passed on from parent to child.

I want to protect my daughter from the sadness that has come before her. I think of the trauma, this inter-generational stain, and of how I want it to stop here, for her, for me. I have gotten things wrong already, as a parent, in my daughter's short life. And I will continue to get things wrong, frequently, I know that is inevitable. But I hope that she can live her life outside of the shadow of shame. For her, I want a life where feeling safe, and heard, and protected is very often true.

UNFINISHED BUSINESS

All that is left of you here are the screw-top jars
you kept in your locker, full of pale blue buttons,
a lifetime's supply salvaged from uniform shirts.

At the end of each shift, you'd tell us
what poor quality they were; kept breaking
or popping off, how the slightest pressure

or hurried fastening would make them fall apart,
break into uneven pieces or how any wear at all
would see the securing threads unravel, leaving

a trail of plastic discs wherever you went.
And when we asked why you saved
those broken shards, you would tell us

about the six foot by six foot collage
you were working on in the shed at home:
your embodiment of the perfect shirt button —

not too brittle, not too thick, the circumference
raised to give a satisfying grip, held secure
with a yard of tightly woven hemp.

MICHAEL SHEEHAN

COLAINN AGUS CORP

Colainn agus corp
Ba ghoradán ar feadh ceathracha seachtain mo chorp,
Dod' chruthú, dod' chothú, dod' choimeád.
Ansin bhí tú scaoilte saor ach fós mothaím an tsreang imleacáin
idir tusa agus mise, dlúthcheangal go deo.
Ba liomsa mo chorp ach anois is leatsa é freisin;
Ní mhairfidh tú gan é, ní mhairfidh tú gan mé.

Féachaim isteach i do shúile dúghorma, iad fós le dath a roghnú
mar tá tú ag forbairt agus ag fiosrú cé tú féin.
Cé mé féin? Nílim cinnte faoi láthair. Is máthair mé.
Cuireann grian na maidine sonas ort
chomh luath agus a bhriseann gathanna tríd na dallóga
déanann tú gáire agus déanaimse gáire.

Caithim súil ar chlog na cistine,
ar laethanta deacra impím ar na snáithidí crágáil leo níos tapúla,
Mé ceaptha a bheith *happy* ach uaireanta tá mé ciaptha
ag an mbuairt, an lagthuirseach, an t-athrá.
Ar laethanta eile, sleamhnaíonn na huaireanta agus leánn nóiméid le chéile,
Guím go moillfidh an t-am nach gcaillfidh mé soicind 's tú ann.

Dúisím i lár na hoíche, mo chroí ag preabadh nach bhfuil tú beo,
Cuirim mo chluas faoi do shrón chun d'análú éadrom a chloisteáil,
Leagaim mo mhéar ar do mhuineál chun do chuisle amhréidh a mhothú,
Dearbhaíonn na mion-ghluaiseachtaí i do mhéiríní beaga ramhra
go bhfuil gach rud i gceart. Céard atá ar siúl i do bhrionglóidí?

Is linne an mhaidin.
Mise le mo chupán caifé, tusa ag ól dríodar órga ó mo chíocha,
Neadaíonn tú isteach i m'ucht, soipríonn tú isteach i m'ascaill,
sólás duit nach bhfaigheann tú áit ar bith eile.
Féachaim síos ar do bheola foirfe, do shrón cnapach, an *philtrum* cothrom eatarthu.
Is linne na splancanna speisialta seo.

Tá dlúthcheangal idir tusa agus mise.
Tú i mo bhaclainn ag siúl timpeall an tí, ag dreapadh an staighre, ag suí ar an leithreas,
ag ól cupán tae, ag crochadh éadaí, ag cromadh le teidí a phiocadh suas.
Braithim go bhfuil mé síoraí seasta, gan stad gan staonadh
Dod' bheathú, dod' bhrúchtadh, dod' chur a chodladh, dod' ní.
Ach fós níl deireadh leis an bhfáinne fí.

Ach tá athdheimhniú sa rithim freisin.
Ar nós dordán an chaidéil cíche,
tugann an sioscadh is sú, sioscadh is sú
faoiseamh ón míchompord.
Mo lámh ag ciorclú do dhroime, mo lúidín ag cuimilt na sramaí de do shúile,
mé ag greadadh mo chos agus tú ar mo ghlúin, suas síos, suas síos.

Anois tá do ghuth aimsithe agat, tá grinntuiscint agam ar gach fuaim.
An *'Mama'* dúilmhear nuair a théim isteach chugat ar maidin,
An cogar mogar a chloisim thar an monatóir,
bímse bodhraithe ag an scréachaíl, béicíl, screadaíl.
Tú ar nós bean sí ag fógairt an bháis nuair a ghearraim banana go mícheart.
Bainne, bia, codladh, clúidín: tuigim fáth na scréiche.

An lá a théann tú ag an bhfeighlí,
Is beag nach mbriseann mo chroí.
Forméadaíonn an tost an folús a fhágann tú i do dhiaidh.

Caithim an lá ag smaoineamh, ag cuimhneamh agus ag machnamh
faoi gach a tharla, atá ag tarlú anois, a bhféadfaí tarlú amach anseo.

Ach ní athróinn rudaí ar ór na cruinne.
Uaireanta ceapaim go bpléascfaidh mo chroí ina smidiríní
le bród, grá, lúcháir agus sonas.
An chéad gháire, an chéad gheit, an chéad fhocal, an chéad fhiacail.
Bhí taithí saoil agam ar na dúáilcí a thiocfadh le máithreachas,
Ach ní raibh taithí ar bith agam ar na súáilcí a thug tú leat ó mo chorp istigh.

ÚNA NÍ CHÁRTHAIGH

CODLADH DEIREANACH

Nuair a thitfeas an codladh deireanach sin orm
Nach dtuigim nach mbeidh ann ach neamhní
Aoibhneas i mbuandorchadas na síoraíochta
Nach mbeidh pianmhar ná scanrúil arís go brách
Gan aithne ná eolas ar neach ná aon ní gan lua
Ní bheidh radharc súl romham ná i mo dhiaidh
Go deo ní bheidh cumha orm ná cronú ionam
Gan aon radharc le feiceáil ná aon tuaim le cluinstin
Ní bheidh aon bholadh le mothú ná aon bhlas i mo bhéal
Gan ábhar le braith arís trí shaol na saol gan chríoch
As seo go brách go deo na ndeor mo shúile druidte
Gan smaointiú a chruthú ná mó shaol a chuimhniú
Suaimhneas síoraí gan deireadh gan tús gan chiall
Molaim daoibh mar sin de mo throcha féin a cheiliúradh
Ná caoin och, och ó domh nó is mise a bheas go breá
I mo bhuanchodladh socair i mo bhuanchodladh sámh.

SEÁN Ó MUIREAGÁIN

WEE PHARMA

GRACE MAGEE

The size of his hands did not change the delicacy of his touch. Tiny white tablets were deftly popped out of the foil and into a brown plastic bottle, faster than I could count, and neater than I could copy. He pressed the flat of his fat finger onto a tablet so that it stuck there when he lifted his hand. Enough force to stick, but not enough to crack.

'You see the numbers on it?' He asked.

I craned over, eyes straining. There was an almost undetectable line down the middle, with 'D' engraved on the top and '22' engraved under.

'That's how you tell the difference between it and aspirin. Aspirin's unmarked.' He gently eased the tablet off his finger with the nail of another.

'What's the line for?'

'That's called the score. It's where you cut them, if you have to.'

He passed the bottle to me to close, and I squeezed the child-proof lock to turn it.

'When you're doing the blister packs, take them slow. I'll be double checking them when you're done, but most people only make mistakes cos they hurry.'

I doubted he'd ever hurried through anything. My boss was the biggest man I'd ever seen, he barely fit in the dispensary. He moved slowly, turning instead of walking. His big belly brushed, but never toppled the stacks of medicine boxes that lined the walls. He'd gone the same grey as the old water-stained tiles on the ceiling, which his hair tickled.

The pharmacy dispensary was a small enough room, and I banged into things all the time, stuck between the walls and the island in the middle. The old fluorescent bulbs didn't provide enough light to properly see the tablets, so he let us use our phones as flashlights. He had thick rimmed glasses and used no flashlight. He lifted boxes of medicine off the wall from behind him without checking the drug or dosage. The dispensary was not organised in any sensible way; I suspected the nonsense order was actually arranged around making sure the most common meds were always within his arms reach.

A blister pack is a sheet of pre-popped medicine, sorted into sections seven across and four down indicating the days of the week and broad strokes of the day. The medicine sits loose in it until the pharmacist checks it against the patient's notes, and seals it with a plastic film. My greatest fear was bumping into someone in the middle of a blister pack, and sending hundreds of quasi-identical tablets flying, to be lost forever on the lino. The other girls in the pharmacy had skinny white scars all across the pads of their fingers from years of popping tablets out of foil. Some of them wore thimbles. None of them would ever forgive a tray being knocked to the floor.

It wasn't a job I was strictly (or legally) qualified for but since the pandemic started, work had quadrupled. Patients who didn't die were suffering from the complications of the virus, and likely would for the rest of their lives. Many of them went to care homes, and care homes needed blister packs. I enjoyed the methodical nature of the work; reading the medication list in the patient's notes, going on an adventure to gather them, and then slowly but surely popping, splitting, and sequestering the tablets into their rightful homes. Like tucking them into bed.

The biggest change that came with working in the dispensary was that my patient-facing duties shrank. I had no complaints about this.

Despite lockdown, more people than ever came into the shop, and I was able to hide from the majority of them in the dispensary. We became the centre of the universe overnight. You couldn't talk to a doctor and you couldn't buy toilet roll, but the local pharmacy never failed. Every morning, there was a line of people waiting for us to open, queuing from the front door to around the corner. A lot of the time, people wouldn't even wait for me to put the key in the lock before they started on me.

'Is the pharmacist in?'

No one was in.

I flashed a polite smile, the first of many, 'Not yet, we open in five! I couldn't get you to put your wee mask on for me, could I?'

We had to shut for an hour at lunch just to get a rest, something we'd never had to do before. If they could detect any signs of life from outside, people would try crawling under the shutters and rapping the glass with their knuckles, like they were at an aquarium. I ate many lunches lying flat on the floor with the lights off. One of the other girls crawled on top of the shelves to eat her curry-half-n-half, crouched up there like Batman.

I became sales clerk, dispensary assistant, and bouncer all at once. Old ladies told me I was the first person they'd spoken to all week and held my hand tightly through double pairs of gloves. Young parents sent us cards and flowers when we managed to get liquid paracetamol for their babies. When we started giving out the vaccine, we got our photos in the paper.

Over the next year and a half, I was put in charge of Mrs McManus' blister pack. She got more meds than the average patient, despite only being in her early seventies. She was basically a spring chicken, compared to the rest of our patients. There were so many tablets in each section that I struggled to seal them at the end. When all her labels and notes were printed, they dragged on the floor behind me as I collected her medication. I didn't mind having such a large chore, because I made up four packs at a time (to last her a month), and this took me from tea break to lunch very nicely. She would phone us at least once a week, and I would talk to her for twenty minutes. Mostly about *the state of things*. She never got my name right, but she got close a few times. She always asked for me.

You really get to know someone when you handle their meds. I knew Mrs McManus didn't like the strawberry flavoured protein shakes, she would take four chocolate, four vanilla. She'd been a smoker and had holes in her oesophagus. She was prescribed a regular supply of morphine patches a week, but I knew she kept one to the side *just in case*, and so had a secret morphine stash in her bedside cabinet. I always made sure her bisoprolol tablets were capsule shaped, not round, because it was easier to swallow. She liked the pink clopidogrels, because it was her favourite colour. She sent cards at Christmas, Easter, and St Bridget's day, and signed them 'Kathy', with hearts, like she was still a little girl. She loved Fleetwood Mac and Elvis. She got mugged once walking to the shops, so she used to carry a hurley stick with her. She had not forgiven Joan Crawford for what she did to her poor daughter. Needless to say, the personal notes section of her file was huge. In the strangest of ways, she was my friend, though there was fifty years between us, and we'd never actually met. Her grown up daughter, Nicola, picked up her blister pack on Thursdays. She always brought her little dog into the shop, let it sniff and shed all over the anti-allergen medications. She told me once I needed to work on my handwriting. I realised then she didn't know I was her mother's friend. How could she? We were the swan's legs of the health service: unseen and hard working. The fact that she didn't know me was testament to our good work. That's what I told myself anyway.

When Mrs McManus died, I knew it had happened the minute Nicola walked in the door. Even her wee dog walked slower. She had two heavy-duty plastic bags filled with unused meds; the secret stash of morphine patches included, as well as unopened blister packs, with my own sloppy handwriting winking at me.

No one wants to say goodbye to their favourite patient, even if it means they're no longer suffering. No one wants to go through all the unused medicine and sort it into different kinds of medical waste bins, medicine you collected only a day ago. No one wants to tear off the labels with the patient's name. A name no longer in use.

'I just wanted to thank all of you,' Nicola started crying before she could get the words out. She took a few shaky breaths, determined to carry on, 'You were all so kind and so thoughtful. I know, towards the end,' she paused, 'her medicines were changing nearly every day, and you had to order those special catheters from England at the last minute so yous had to stay open late, and I just wanted to say we appreciated everything...'

I didn't hear the rest of what she had to say because I noticed her dog was taking a piss on the floor. Such a small animal, such a big puddle. Fifty percent of that beast must've been liquid. After hugs and gentle reassurances, and carefully navigating her out of the shop so that she didn't spot the pond of piss, I got the mop and some bleach. I spent the next hour vivisecting Mrs McManus' blister packs. I quietly said my goodbyes to her as I dissolved her oxycodone into unusable slime.

A kind of fugue settled on me. The smell of the denaturing kit was making me queasy, and everything was annoying. That's probably why I nipped out to the shop front so quickly when I heard the door open.

In came a completely nondescript man and his young daughter. She was maybe five years old. She had an iPad in her hands in one of the big chunky cases they make for kids, but instead of watching it, she was holding it up over her head, like she was scanning the room.

'Hello.' I said, to which there was no response.

The man came closer, and his daughter took little hurried steps to keep up.

'You,' He licked his lips and breathed hard through his mouth, 'are under a Citizen's Arrest.'

I couldn't have possibly heard him correctly, 'Excuse me?'

'This is a cease-and-desist letter from the local community.' He slid a folded piece of paper to me, under the plastic barrier. 'To bring an end to the poison and filth you have been peddling to our children and our elderly.'

I opened the paper up and skimmed the large font paragraph. Buzzwords included *vaccine, government, communists,* and *toxin.* Ignoring that these were mostly antonyms, he continued,

'You are currently being livestreamed.'

That caught my attention. I looked back down at the little girl and her iPad. Its beady little black camera held my reflection.

'We know where you work. We know your name.'

My nametag. The second I remembered it, it suddenly felt very heavy.

He pointed right at me, 'There are hundreds of us, and we won't stand for it. We won't be cattle, we won't be test subjects. We are free men, in a free country, and you have one night to destroy your vaccine supplies, before we come back here, and settle it ourselves!' He pounded his fist on the till.

I'll admit, I was scared. So scared I didn't even contradict him when he said *it's a free country,* because, by definition, Northern Ireland isn't.

I didn't hear my boss coming towards us, but there he was all of a sudden.

'Out.' He pointed towards the door. 'Out!'

The girl turned the iPad towards him and I saw him mentally restrain himself from smacking her.

'Take your wee gremlin with ya! Out of my shop!'

'Are you the owner of this establishment?' The man leaned forward, his breath fogging up the plastic partition. 'Because if so, you are to answer to this community for...'

He didn't finish his thought, because when my boss stepped around the partition towards him, he scampered, only remembering his child at the last minute. He yanked her little wrist so hard, I thought she'd cry out, but she just kept looking at us, completely rapt, iPad held aloft. They walked right through the spot where I'd been hugging Nicola. The pissy mop water had only just dried.

My boss followed them out onto the street, but didn't give chase once they headed away from the shop. He stood for a moment, fuming, before stalking back inside.

The other girls joined me at the till.

'Who was that?'

'What did he want?'

'Was he serious?'

They grabbed the letter and were tugging it between them when my boss snatched it off them,

'Don't tear it! The police will want to see it.'

'What did he mean by that?' One of the girls asked, distraught, eyes wide. 'Are we in danger?'

Boss didn't say anything, he was already dialling.

One of the girls whispered, 'They burnt out the pharmacy over on West Street, y'know. Came at night and burnt the whole place down. There's nothing but the graffiti left on the walls. I knew the locum there; she had to move. They put threats through her letter box, followed her home from work.'

Another girl started to quietly cry, the others took her out the back. I flipped the sign on the door to CLOSED.

When the police came, they told us we weren't the first pharmacy that day to have had a visit from this man. Or at least, a man and a child, all on the same mission. They'd been active all over the city. They reassured us that very little would come from his threats, but they wanted to talk to me personally.

'Now love, we can't be certain that he was actually livestreaming to any legitimate site,' The policeman explained to me. 'Most likely, it was an empty threat. Or at the very worst, just Facebook. If anyone saw it, they probably wouldn't be able to see your nametag. Not with the dirt of your divider, anyway!' He tried joking, pointing over his shoulder at the partition with his thumb. He wasn't funny but he wasn't wrong either. It was looking a little foggy. I'd have to clean it later.

'Now, if anyone gets in contact with you about this, you let us know, okay? Organisations like this operate on fear. You might get messages threatening to rape you or something, but it's all stuff and nonsense, okay love? How are you getting home?'

'Bus,' I said. 'I always get the bus here and back.'

He pursed his lips, 'Maybe for the next week or so, you could get someone to give you a lift. We could do it for you today, if you like. Get a ride in a real police car! You'll be able to send your mates photos of you in it!'

I felt oddly sorry for him. He must have seen my gaunt stare and heard how hollow his words were ringing. He was completely fucking useless but he couldn't help it.

'No, thank you.' I could only imagine the fuss if my neighbours saw me in the back of a cop car. 'I'll get a lift with one of the girls.'

Once the police left, the boss didn't make us reopen the shop. As we locked up, I saw him load the minifridge from the dispensary into his car, vaccines inside and all.

Before we turned the computers off, I opened Mrs McManus' profile, half out of habit, before I remembered. I thought for a second I could hear the phone ringing. Thought I could smell her destroyed medicine still lingering in the air. I deleted all her personal notes to free up storage.

I didn't ask anyone for a lift home in the end. The girls would want to talk about it and the boss would drive in silence, and neither appealed to me. It took me twice as long to walk to the bus stop because I kept stopping and looking over my shoulder. It gets so dark so early in the winter. The old amber streetlamps can't give off much light. Each gap between them seemed longer than usual. At the bus stop shelter, there were a dozen white stickers stuck to the wall, arranged in the shape of a cross. Each of them said, 'BELIEVE NO LIES. DEUTERONOMY 32:32.'

They hadn't been there that morning. When the bus pulled up, I saw it was decorated with painted rainbows and superheroes, and a banner that said, 'Thank you our essential workers!'

HER WAVES

I caught her last breath in a small,
copper-topped, glass jar.
I balanced it on the edge of my universe,
near the fire-eyed photo of us.

I twist it open now and release the sounds,
my mother's spittle evaporating
as her tongue-wet finger glances off
the face of the Russell Hobbs.

I hear her cutlery lying in lines
like resting bone-handled soldiers,
their teeth a-chatter
in the pull of the busy kitchen drawer.

I hear the crunch of the knife
as she cuts red apples into boaty wedges,
the blade pulled back towards
the flesh of her thumb.

And the chipped enamel of her teapot lid
as it cackles itself into position,
sealing the hot breath of the vessel,
ready for the sacred draw.

There, there, she whispers
into nettle-stung children's ears,
a pregnant cloth, fat with frozen peas,
pressed cold, removing thin heat.

Now the jar is empty and silent,
the vibrant air inhaled deep and long.
Her waves skittle across the line between lung void
and the tumble of my red blood cells.

RORY DUFFY

BLIZZARD YEAR

In the beginning, snow covered the mountains like the lace tablecloth
in her mother's kitchen. She hung around under the eaves and watched
as the blizzard took the land, filling in the empty places like sanding sugar,
making the world whole. She liked to think of herself
as a regular Snowflake Bentley, catching the six-sided crystals
on her mittens, telling each one before they melted, *you were beautiful.*

After the first week, time lost meaning, fracturing like ice
on the edges of the river where she and her boots tried their luck.
White was her favorite color. She had never been in love.
At night, after her Daddy went to sleep, she and her mother
ate Twizzlers they had hidden away from her brothers,
watching Clark Gable and Vivien Leigh break each other's hearts.

Atlanta burned, and her father slept, and they crept over the cold floors
in their sock feet. The heating kicked off and on and off.
When the nighttime silence threatened an avalanche,
they slunk off, out of the house, sleek as foxes. There were no stars.
The fences, ditches, road had gone, leaving only the impermanent patterns
of wind on snow, curving and rippling. Lying in the road, they ascended

to heaven, beating their wings, listening to the feathery quiet descending
around them. Icy dancers settled on their lashes, dissolved on their tongues.
Under the black snow-sky, she pictured Rhett carrying Scarlett off,
up those grand stairs, small fists making ineffective contact with his white shirt.
How his eyes sparkled. How hers flashed. *To be loved like that,* she thought,
closing her eyes. When someone just had to have you, knew what you wanted

better than you did yourself. Surely, that was love.

Now, the snow is gone, and the girl is gone, but not her notions.

Lying on the hearthstone in her lover's house she tries to make him understand this significance. *Like lace*, she says, *do you know what I mean?* He tells her not to talk so much, that she's ruining the moment. She feels like an instrument he never learned how to play. Watching the coals, she presses her hands
  to the fireguard

and holds, holds. When she takes them away, they're blistered, but she
  doesn't feel it.

I'm dead, nothing can hurt me, she thinks. She repeats this mantra, like
  a prayer.

FIONA TRACEY

SINKING TO MINOR SWING

FIJA CALLAGHAN

When I died, I lost:

1500 books, including a first edition copy of Peter Pan (est. total €16,000)
1 pair of red patent Repetto ballet flats, size 36 (€280)
1 unfinished poetry collection, provisionally titled Night-blooming Roses
(€50 or so)
1 city-centre apartment, with balcony (priceless)
1 future
1 vintage gramophone (value unknown)

When we moved in together, he brought most of his furniture with him.
I had two suitcases—one of clothes, the other of books—and a vintage
gramophone secured to the top of the small suitcase with bootlaces.

I put the clothes in one corner, and the books in another corner,
and the gramophone beneath the window, and thought, *Yes. Home. I am
home.*

I'm a first-year undergrad sitting in one of those after-theatre bars
where I don't know anybody. It's too loud and it smells like spilled liquor.
I'm sipping orange juice because it's the only thing they serve with no
alcohol in it. My housemate, who begged me to come so she wouldn't be
alone, is late.

Everybody seems to know everybody else. There is a disproportionate
number of fedoras.

'You could read something too,' she said. 'It's chill, everyone's really
supportive.'

The very thought makes me dizzy. I never share my poems with
anyone.

'Well, just come and cheer me on then.'

And I say, 'Yeah, okay.' Because I have nothing else to do on a
Saturday night.

The bartender thinks I'm pregnant. She glanced at my stomach when I asked for orange juice.

'Driving?' she said.

I shook my head, realising a beat too late I should have just said yes.

Someone's stepping onto the little dais that serves as a stage. He speaks into the mic and welcomes everyone. My housemate isn't here, and if I try to leave now, everyone will stare at me.

He's wearing a fedora over a shock of golden hair. I've never seen that colour on a man before. His pinstripe jacket is all sharp lines to hide the softness of his face. He is not beautiful, but something about him makes me wonder if I could be. As though I, the bartender, everyone in the room has been stunningly beautiful this whole time only no one thought to tell us. I wonder what it would be like to feel the softness of him beneath my fingers.

He recites a poem into the mic. It has words like ephemeral, superfluous, and artifice. I count artifice twice. I don't understand it very well, but I like the sound the words make all tangled up together. I want to wrap them around myself and fall asleep in them.

It's two in the morning and we're walking near College Green over a fresh dusting of snow. I keep looking over my shoulder at the marks our boots have left behind—two perfect rows of silhouettes on a canvas tinted lamplight-bronze. I feel that we have in some small way marked the world as our own. That this still, silent night is offering it to us in all its limitless potential.

'Your mum called,' he says one evening, when I arrive home from work. 'There's a message.'

Our home has grown full of more books than I could ever fit in a suitcase. Cheap paperbacks and first editions scoured from bookshop basements stand proudly side by side. Everywhere I turn are small reminders that I am here, I am real: wildflowers that I picked for him, hanging upside down to dry; a bronze plaque with a claddagh on it that I found at a charity shop for six euro; a poem I wrote, scribbled onto a restaurant napkin and framed. My poetry is not refined and elevated like his, but it makes me feel as though I have offered some small gift to the world, some payment for taking up space in it.

My feet ache from a ten-hour shift at the boutique, but I pause in the doorway. My mother never calls.

It's not until much later, after dinner, after asking about his day, after making love slowly and quietly on the balcony under the stars, that I listen to the message. My mother has heard from an old mutual friend that my father is sick. Very sick.

'Maybe you should call him,' she says.

I thought the world would hurt less when I was dead.

I thought the agony of loss would soften into dull-edged oblivion. I thought that all the questions I had would become, if not answered, less important than they'd been before.

Death was less like oblivion and more like anhedonia. This was a word I learned from one of his poems. I wandered through the apartment, my ghostly feet passing through cardboard boxes as he packed up our life. I watched him lock the claddagh away with packing tape, untie the wildflowers and press them into the compost bin. Little by little, the walls were stripped down until it was like I was never there at all.

He sold the gramophone. A man with thick plastic glasses and sideburns came to take it away. I tried to stop him, but my voice was an empty murmur on the wind.

The autumn I turn fourteen, the guidance counsellor calls me into her office.

She says, 'This needs to stop.'

I blink up at her, shuffling through possibilities in my mind. I have no idea what she's talking about.

'You can't be drinking alcohol before school. You're here to learn, and if you can't bring yourself to do that, we need to think about whether or not you should be here at all.'

I'm still completely at sea. 'I don't drink alcohol,' I say. I add that I'm fourteen, and wonder if she's confused me for someone else.

The counsellor gives me an impatient look. 'Your teachers can smell it on your clothes.'

Understanding crashes into me. For a brief moment I consider trying to explain my mother, the scent of her that clings to the walls, the white-hot anger that flares and roars without warning. The way I get through one day at a time by making myself small.

The moment passes, and instead I just look down and nod.

That night I get into the shower and scrub and scrub and scrub. I start keeping extra clothes in the back of my locker.

Two months after we move in together, Bindweed Quarterly writes me to say they want to publish one of my poems.

I read the message three times. Somebody wants to put my words in a real literary journal. Once my hands are steady and I'm sure I didn't imagine it, I run into the other room to tell him.

He puts his arms around me. 'I'm so proud of you,' he says. I try to think if anyone has been proud of me before, and come up blank.

To celebrate, we put a record on the gramophone. The cool cascade of *Minor Swing* floats into the air. He offers me his hand, and together we kick our heels up in the living room, laughing and tripping over each other's feet. I'm so happy I feel as though my heart could burst.

My high school graduation is about to begin, and I'm the last one to enter the auditorium. I stand outside in the carpark, in a shimmering dress I've borrowed from the school's drama department, scanning the row of vehicles again and again. When at last I hear the voices settle I think, *maybe he's already inside.*

My mother is there, sober and smiling. Her handbag occupies the seat beside her. She catches my eye and her smile dims. Later, she will call my father and yell into the phone, and I'll want to tell her it's fine, it's no big deal, but the words won't come.

He does make it seven months later. I brush my hair and braid it, then loosen it, then braid it again. As we walk by the seaside, he tells me that his girlfriend is pregnant.

I didn't know my father had a girlfriend. We spend the afternoon wandering through the shopping centre, looking at baby clothes.

'I thought you hated the guy,' he says when I tell him about the message.

'I don't hate him.' I turn the words over in my mouth, prod them with my tongue, searching for the off-flavours of a lie. Hate is too simplistic,

I decide. A single, reverberating note.

'Are you going to go see him?'

I haven't seen my father in more than ten years. His daughter is thirteen now. I saw her in a songwriting competition on TV.

I say 'I don't know,' and put the kettle on. I'll think about it later. I've got time.

I learn how to tell the bad days from the Really Bad Days. My mother hurts me very rarely; more often it's dishes, wine glasses, picture frames. I wait until she disappears into her bedroom, and then I pick my way around the broken shards, knowing they'll have been cleaned up by the time I get back.

Today she doesn't disappear into her bedroom. Instead, she knocks on my door.

'Just a minute,' I say, 'I'm getting changed.'

I know I don't have very long, so I grab every breakable thing I see and shove it under my bed.

'Come in,' I say, as if everything's fine. The room suddenly feels very small.

She asks me a question. At this point I know that anything I say will be the wrong thing to say, so I don't answer. The silence hums, crackles, snaps.

It's like watching a tornado trapped inside the body of a five-foot-tall woman. I stay very, very still as it tears across my bookshelves, my dresser, pulls the magazine cutouts from the walls. A thumbtack rains down with them, and I make a mental note not to step on it later. She yanks a mirror off the wall and I think, *Drat. I should have grabbed that.*

She's breathing hard, and for a moment I think it might be over. Then her eyes land on the gramophone. I stiffen, and my fingers tighten at my side. I force myself not to move. To react is fatal.

The gramophone topples over with a crack. The wide brass horn clatters as it snaps off the wooden base. She kicks it across the room. I can hardly breathe.

The horn is still ringing distantly, and as it fades, the gale dies down. My mother looks around at the carnage as if seeing it for the first time. She chokes back a sob and runs from the room. I hear the front door open and shut, the rattling of keys.

I don't know why she's upset, I think. *It wasn't her gramophone.*

When the house is still, I take the brass horn in my arms and finally allow myself to cry.

When my poetry pamphlet wins a chapbook contest—€200 and publication—I start to notice that something's wrong.

'That's great.' His voice is flat and he doesn't look at me.

I'd been thinking about the red ballet flats I wanted to buy with my winnings, but I stop and frown.

'Isn't it?'

He's not having much luck with his submissions. Modern poetry is too subjective; it doesn't appreciate form. His use of figurative language and Keatsean rhetoric passes over the heads of most editors.

Privately, I wonder if his aim is too narrow. He submits only to the New Yorker, Threepenny, the Paris Review. I once suggested trying some smaller magazines, but he told me that would be a waste because it would use up first publication rights without any exposure or prestige in return. He said this like it should be obvious. I said oh, okay.

'It's just a chapbook,' I tell him. 'It's like a glorified business card.'

I'm not sure why I'm saying these things. I thought he would be happy.

He smiles, and nods, and everything is alright again. 'Can we put on some music?' I say.

'I'm exhausted,' he says. 'I'm going to bed.'

I drifted through memories.

Some of them seemed more real to me here, in this in-between place, than they did while I was living them. The sharp crack of breaking glass; the creeping chill of loneliness in a high school carpark; the simmering terror of loss.

I looked at the girl I was and understood, for the first time, how those moments shaped the woman she grew to become. I understood that when my mother did those things to our home, she was stopping herself from doing them to me. I understood that my father saw in his new daughter a chance to start again, free from mistakes and the weight of lost years.

I understood that the man I loved was never going to love me in the way that I loved him.

I curled up in a ball of smoke and shadow and ached for all the things I didn't understand.

The phone rings in my ear. It has a tinny, faraway sound and I imagine it reaching through the void of space, across highways and rivers, to the farmhouse my father shares with his wife and daughter. His family.

I don't know what to say. Sorry to hear that you're dying? Do you need anything? Why did you leave me?

I have thirty years of unspoken questions, and all of them turn to ash in my mouth.

His daughter answers. I recognise her voice from the TV show.

'Hello?' she says.

'Hi. Hello.' I struggle for words. 'Is Dad there?'

'Who's this?'

I tell her my name.

There is a long pause. Then she says, 'Who?'

I hang up.

Not long after I turn nineteen, my mother announces she's moving in with her boyfriend. I see her less and less. Sometimes she's gone for days at a time.

I fix my eyes on the frayed threading on my jeans. It's not a Really Bad Day, so if I'm careful, I can dodge the worst of it.

'I can't keep living like this,' she says.

'You don't appreciate anything I do for you,' she says.

'You don't talk to me.'

'You don't look at me.'

'It's like living with a stranger.'

She says some other things too, but I don't hear because I'm busy mentally sifting through my bank account, wondering how I'm going to pay for this apartment on my own.

She leaves most of the furniture behind, and I sell it piece by piece to get by. Dining table: €75. Three chairs: €40. Standing lamp: €8. I eat ready meals standing up at the kitchen countertop. Soon the only thing left is a clumsily repaired gramophone, looking like a relic from another age.

For a while, he keeps his other women hidden from me. After a few months he stops bothering, and I can smell them on his clothes, feel the shape of them in his touch. I stop telling him when my poetry is accepted, and then I stop sending it out altogether, but I'm too late. The damage is done. I've already driven a wedge between us that I can never take back.

I want so much to be what he needs, but I don't know how.

We lie beside each other in the dark, and I trace the shape of him in the shadows.

'Please don't leave me,' I whisper. It's so quiet that I'm not sure if I really said it at all, or if I only imagined it.

When I'm seven, I go to stay with my father for a week in the country. He comes to pick me up in a mud-splattered truck cancerous with rust, and I delight in the novelty of sitting in a vehicle. The city whips by the window until it becomes golden farmland.

There is so much space, not only outside but in his three-bedroomed, high-ceilinged house, that I am dizzy with it. I want to explore every corner of this new world, but my eyes are drawn to a vintage gramophone standing in the corner.

'That was your grandad's,' he says. 'Here, let's put something on.'

My father chooses a record. 'Do you know Django Reinhardt?'

I shake my head.

He lowers the needle and music fills the room. It's like nothing I've ever heard before. He bows and offers me his hand and I giggle, suddenly shy.

I like feeling his big, safe hands over my small ones as we dance around the room. Happiness bubbles up inside me like fizzy pop. I want to stay in this farmhouse and dance with him forever.

When the song ends, I make him play it over and over again.

Afterwards he says, 'You can take that with you, if you want. Set it up in your room. I never use it.'

My happiness turns to awe. I've never owned anything so wonderful in all of my long seven years. I imagine how it will look in my bedroom, catching the first rays of morning light.

'Thank you,' I say nervously. The words feel too small for such a momentous gift. 'Can I try putting a record on?'

He teaches me how to lift the needle, suspended in mid-air, and then let go. 'Never put it down on the record,' he says, 'or you might scratch it.' Just hold it in your fingers and let go.

It takes me a few tries to get it right. *Minor Swing* fills the room. I grab his hand and we kick our heels up until it's time for dinner.

He's going to stay with his parents for the weekend. He says he hasn't seen them in a while. They live three hours away in a commuter town with gardens and red-brick houses. I ask if he wants me to go with him.

He's silent so long I become tongue-tied. I know that whatever I say next, no matter what it is, will be the wrong thing.

Finally, he says, 'I've already asked someone.' He pushes his dinner around with his fork. 'I'd like them to meet her.'

There's nothing I can say that won't be the wrong thing to say, that won't tear us farther apart. Suddenly I'm choking and I can't stop. There is a rushing deep inside of me, and I think of the tornado that tore through my mother all those years ago. For the first time I realise that it lives in me too.

I don't remember putting my shoes on, but I am outside in the grey afternoon light. The world has a hazy, underwater quality to it. I stumble into the street and hear a car horn, loud and insistent and sharp.

In books they always say 'It all happened so fast'. It doesn't happen fast. There's a moment, a shimmering prism of time, in which I could step out of harm's way. I hold the moment in my hands and stare into it, and the moment stares back.

Nah, screw it, I think finally. *It's better this w—*

The man in the hipster glasses loaded my gramophone into the back of a truck. The truck said, Robinson's Antiques. I watched from the upstairs window.

The truck idled, like a purring monster, waiting.

I walked through the gutted apartment, touching misty fingers to empty bookshelves, barren walls. The only safe, happy home I'd ever known. I wondered where he would go now. Who he would become.

When the truck roared to life, I was there like a breath of wind. I did not look back.

Robinson's Antiques is dusty and cluttered and filled with stories. I wander through the soft, welcoming silence on a faded carpet the colour of snow. My steps make no sound. I like the quiet.

After the shop closes and the salespeople go home—to families, loved ones, lives—I hold the gramophone needle carefully in mid-air and let go. *Minor Swing* spills into the dark.

I spin myself into the lonely golden glow of the streetlamp, and kick my heels up, and think, *Yes. Home. I am home.*

BEALACH AN BHÁIS

Seachain an cathú an chíor a thógáil den talamh.
Fág i do dhiaidh í díreach mar atá sí sa slodán.
Ná bí ag súgradh 's ag slaparnach timpeall uirthi.
Caith na locháin de léim agus ná lig don bhean sí
An dallamullóg a chur ort.
Ní ghéillfidh do choirníní gleoite dá cíor.
Ní dhéanfaidh an ceann seo an gnó.
Seachain an chíor a scuabfadh chun siúil thú.

Is cíor ghéar í atá i ndán do chréatúr bocht tinn.
Idir an dá linn fillfidh an bhean chaointe anseo anocht.
Scuabfaidh sí siar a cuid gruaige faoin saileach shilte
Ag cíoradh 's ag caoineadh,
Ag caoineadh 's ag cíoradh .
Druid siar ón gcaoineadh sin más suaimhneas intinne atá uait.
Druid siar, druid siar as bealach an bháis.

CAITRÍONA LANE

GHOST STORY

After Willa Cather

When the dancing stopped
we raced across the frozen plain.
In our sled the bride and groom,
my brother and I — both groomsmen

for the day. Four sleds followed,
made slower by the weight of guests.
We heard but could not see the wolves
— just like the preacher said.

Soon they swarmed on those behind
and tore them all to pieces.
My brother flung the reins to me
and threw the couple to the pack.

I felt a lightness like we just unloaded
wood and turned the team for home.
I saw the glimmer of the inn,
the chapel lit for vespers

— two joys extinguished in a trice.
I heard the manic whip, the circling swarm,
my words flying with the snow,
What have we done? What have we done?
— then leapt into their jaws.

FRANK FARRELLY

LIKE A ROMANCE IN ITALICS

MARY WILKINSON

She's lying in bed listening to him rustle about downstairs in the kitchen. He's most likely whistling softly as he reaches for the coffee filters and the coffee jar, carefully pouring water into the reservoir. While he waits for the coffee to brew, she's certain he'll go sit at the kitchen table and start scrolling through his phone. Sports. CNN. Wordle. He usually plays Wordle while he's waiting for the coffee to brew. Occasionally he doesn't and when he brings her the coffee she'll ask him, 'Play Wordle yet?'

'No.' He'll answer back as if he's reluctant to admit it, as if he's disappointed with himself even though he still manages to ask her if she's played.

This time she'll answer no. She finished reading the Nabokov book instead. 'I finished it,' she says. 'And I don't know why you didn't like the ending. I thought it flawless. You know,' she says, reaching for the book and riffling to the last page, to the part written as if in stage directions, 'silent scene: door – wide open. Table – thrust away from it...' and she hurriedly reads the entire paragraph aloud because he's already turning to leave and she wants to get it all out before he does. She knows he's anxious to go back downstairs to play Wordle. She can hardly remember when he would come upstairs with two cups of coffee and get back into bed to talk with her about nothing in particular. Lazy, meandering talk that went nowhere, wasn't intended to go anywhere. The words fluid and loose like they didn't care either way. No measure. No second guessing. How long ago was that?

She's thinking about the book again. Trying to figure out what seems to be missing in it. Something important. But it might be a dream she's having. All of this. The open book on the bed. The man in the doorway. The curtains pulled apart. It's a habit of his pulling open the curtains when he brings her coffee. Even when it's pitch dark outside. She still teases him for doing that, asking him 'Why would you open the curtains? You're mad. No one else around here does that only you.' He never responds. He just doesn't. She likes that about him. How nothing bothers him. It just flows right off of him.

What is it about Nabokov's book that she can't reconcile? It's hard to even concentrate on Wordle. She has a starter word. Candy. Two vowels, not one. He'd be quick to remind her of that. She's certain she loved him when he repeated it like a child in a classroom might, A, E, I, O, U and sometimes Y. How many times has he reiterated that rule to her? How many years now? Years. So many. A dream maybe.

Over breakfast she says, 'What about the book?'

'What? What are you talking about?'

'You know how the book is all about desire but he barely mentions the word love. But is desire love? Or is it a precursor of love? Nabokov keeps going on about the need and the craving. What about after the craving? The time it takes to reach beyond the craving to the love bit. You don't see much love. It's all about pleasure. The sex. Using people to get what they want. To only satisfy their needs. Yet nobody ends up with anything.'

He's agreeing with her now. Saying 'You know you're right.' And it could be she's feeling a little important then to have come up with a topic. Something they can talk about instead of Wordle.

'Did you finish Wordle?' He asks her again.

'No, remember I was trying to figure the Nabokov book out. The love thing.'

'Oh right.' He says and gets up from the table and walks to the window and looks out while she's thinking it has to be a dream.

These days. The time it takes to move into every second like in slow motion. Washing the dishes. Tossing out the cold coffee. Stacking the clean white cups in the dresser. Bleaching the sink to get rid of the coffee stains. Wiping the condensation off the glass. Peering out into the navy-blue day looking for clues on how to proceed. Knowing she'll never be clever enough or strategic enough to sort things out like he does. Like he does when he plays Wordle. So often she doesn't get it and uses up every chance available to her. Runs out of guesses while all the possible words remain stubbornly, mischievously silent in her head.

They still manage to talk though. Like the night before when they had been eating a particularly bony fish for dinner, he reminisced about when his father took him on a fishing trip to Idaho. He went on about the camper van and his stepmother and how she'd brush her hair for the longest time before going to bed. Her laughter in the darkness as she lay alongside his father confused and scared him and made him long for his mother at home in California and for the shade of the pepper trees when he played in the yard. Anyhow, he went on to tell her about the trout he caught and his father cooking it and how, as he was eating it, a bone got caught in his throat. He said his father had to take him to the nearest doctor twenty miles away to get the bone dislodged. She liked him telling her this. She must have loved him right there. Or did she just feel sorry for him? She wonders why it took him all these years to tell her the story about the fish bone getting stuck. Although there was no reason to feel sorry for him. She reminded herself of that. He was only relaying how painful it is to get a fish bone stuck in your throat.

They did this sometimes. But she did it more. Associated things with the past. From the twenty years or the twenty years before that. Or even the twenty years before that. She can pick images up and tell him without any censor whatsoever.

Opening the book in her mind when eating tomatoes, she'll say, 'There were tomatoes in a greenhouse.'

She can even relate how stiflingly hot it was. She always expresses how she might be imagining that. The part about the heat. The intense heat of that summer in Cork where she was born. But she's pretty certain about the man who grew the tomatoes. How his name was Mr Barker and how he owned a cat. A big glaring cat that scratched at her arm and made her cry. She never liked cats after that.

And if she gets a package delivered to her in the post, she'll say, 'I remember the first package I ever got. My sister sent it to me. She lived in London and she sent me a dress. It was blue and green like the sea.' Snippets of remembering. Then nothing. For a time. Only hazy dreams, random memories.

And then they might spend some time talking about potential five letter words for Wordle. He always thinks he's chosen the perfect word. Like he has it all figured out. She knows he's not happy when she occasionally wins. It seems to be the only thing he gets worked up about.

The love word rarely features though. Mostly it goes unspoken and she's okay with that too. But it just can't be easily forgotten, relegated to the bottom drawer. Can it? It has to come about now and then, surface in conversation. Rise naturally to recognition without any reason whatsoever. Without anyone dying or without feeling you're forced to say it but just simply forming your lips around the word, the letters, the L, the tip of one's tongue lightly flicking the front teeth. Then the other letters, like a romance in italics follow to gracefully loop together, to gather pace. To become fully formed. Once she Googled a five-letter synonym for love, something to fit with Wordle rules but in the middle of desire, lust, fondness, tenderness, doting, infatuation, benevolence, kindness—she could only find one word with five letters: amour. Somehow it just didn't work for her although it had the right amount of vowels necessary for possible Wordle success.

Maybe that's why she's had a hard time with the book. The Nabokov book. Because it seems to her that love, real love is hard to write about. Real love is when you include someone else so that someone becomes infused in your bones and your hair and your skin so much so that you can't really separate or figure out where things end or begin.

Say for example a sudden illness occurs and she goes to visit the man in hospital, the one who usually brings her coffee in bed. It's serious. The reason he's in the hospital. There are procedures and all kinds of awful stuff to contend with and a whole new vocabulary takes hold and words she could never use in Wordle suddenly become second nature to her. There is blood in bags to be emptied and other challenging things she had never imagined in normal times. And the woman stands at the end of the bed watching the man. He's sitting up wearing one of those undignified paper gown things. And every time he moves, she can hear the rubber sheet groan beneath the bed sheets and she understands how uncomfortable it has to be especially because it's a beautiful summer's day outside and sunlight streams through the window overlooking a park where children play ball and people walk their dogs. She's brought a freshly laundered pair of pyjamas so she tries to help him out of the stupid gown to change into the pyjamas but there are all kinds of wires and drips and monitors to hinder her progress. Still, she keeps on trying because she knows the cotton will feel cool and delicious against his clammy skin. And then there's this, the final scene, an unadorned stage with two people, the two of them facing each other, arms extended, exit door ajar, white glow flickering in corridor beyond, a fading light beyond that. And then. Silence.

ANCHOR STITCH

Once he had asked and I said yes, we flew
to London, Mum and I, budget, red-eye,
trawled the costumeries of Soho,
the Liberty remnant troughs, returning that night
with six metres of duck-egg satin, two of lace chiffon.

We borrowed a form from her friend Joann
and for six months, I shared
a bedroom with that silent twin,
draped in muslin mock-ups, pinned
with panels of interfacing, lining.

I worked with ceremony
in cotton gloves like a magician —
shaping cap sleeves, scoop neck, empire line,
added thirty covered buttons along the spine,
three hidden tapes to bustle up the train.

Afterwards, the dress became a headless Havisham
stuffed pert with acid-free tissue paper
in a vacuum-sealed box with viewing panel,
waiting in the attic for a daughter to claim her
and now, failing that, staying on as ballast.

EILÍN DE PAOR

BEARNÚ

tá brí do shúl sáite go daingean im ghrua
agus craiceann d'ordóige ag tabhairt uaidh leis an scríobadh
agus feicim na focail ag éirí chun d'fhiacla
– beidh pian iontu

scrúdaím matáin chasta do cheannaghaidhe
ag guibhe go leáfaidh an tsnaidhm ina haoibh
go bhfeice mé an athuair do liopaí ina gcuar
is an tobairín beannaithe lena dtaobh

níl uaim ach breith romham ar do cholainn gheal ghlé
mo bhos a bhualadh go bog thar bhearna do bhéil
chun nach fíor fós na focail nár chuala an t-aer
chun gur faide uainn anocht ná inné

ach brúnn tú lann do theanga chun cinn
an rinn ag gearradh trí d'anáil go binn
sánn tú do shúile gléghorma tríom
agus baineann do chuid focal deoir as an tost

déanaim dínn dúch le tú a choinneáil mar a bhí tú
an oíche úd faoin mbraillín is do bholg le mo dhroim
nuair a bhuail tú do bhos go bog thar mo bhéal
chun nach n-éalódh uaim siolla de m'anam

EOIN MC EVOY

MARKET IN DRUMBEG

Sitting in a parking lot in Drumbeg
between homemade beeswax candles
and artisanal grilled cheese stalls
we fall out of love.
I spend our time together hiding
the messages on my phone
from the boy ten years younger
who tells me all the things
you used to tell me
and whose house I
spend mornings at, naked
and ashing cigarettes
into empty water bottles.
I could never imagine him
at this market filled with organic
soap and hand-sewn baby bibs.
These markets are where we are,
buying fresh eucalyptus for the shower
even though it goes moldy
and gets in the way of the taps.
Us and the other couples in their 30s
orbit around the stalls with coffee
made in a horsebox.
The difference between us
and them isn't our taste
in homewares or decor,
it's that we speak about ourselves
in the English we learned
at school, not at home.

ALANNA OFFIELD

SMOKER'S COUGH

MARY MORRISSY

'Light?' she asks as she sees the mop-haired young man standing a couple of feet away tap his chest and pockets as if engaged in some religious ritual.

He nods.

She doesn't know his name—these post-docs come and go in the department so regularly and aren't here long enough to acquire personalities, let alone names.

She holds out her lighter and, in an oddly tender gesture, he cups her wrist to hold her hand steady—is she developing a shake?—as he lights his cigarette. It feels transgressive. When was the last time... People aren't supposed to be touching like this, are they? Something about his ringed curls and the way he has to bend towards her because of his height—or because of hers? Is she shrinking?—makes her think of Enrico. Enrico, of all people!

Post-doc is smoking a rollie, thin and dinged-looking, and without a roach. Here, she wants to say, have a proper cigarette—you'll haul and haul on that yoke and it will never deliver satisfaction—but she doesn't, for fear it would be inappropriate. Post-doc smiles and retreats. They stand, the required distance apart, facing the glass doors of the fire exit. The irony! She sees her expression as she inhales. It looks like it hurts her to smoke. The anorexic hollow of her cheeks makes it seem as if the cigarette is smoking her.

Post-doc holds his thin home-made cheroot delicately between the tips of his fingers and sips on it. A social smoker. Wait for it, there'll be a fit of coughing soon.

When she was younger, in the black-and-white world, she remembered waking to morning-after twinges (along with an ashen mouth and sandpapery throat) when a whole pack or two might have disappeared. But people shared and bummed all the time then, so she couldn't be sure she'd smoked every single one herself. But apart from that, in almost 50 years, she's never regretted a smoke.

They've left their mark, of course, and she's not talking about her lungs. She has no interest in her inner life; her physical inner life, that is. Whatever the damage, it's done now. Once when she was at a conference in Perugia, a young man smelling of cologne, handing out flyers outside a perfume shop, offered her a free skin consultation. 'A smoker, I see,' he said disapprovingly, as he tilted her head towards the light, pointing to the puckered fan-spread of lines above her upper lip. And look, she doesn't have to be told, she smells bad. She doesn't like the whiff of herself. But what woman of 68 is totally fragrant? Hence the disguising strategies. The mouthwash, the body spray, the heavy musky perfume.

But she would explain, if anyone were prepared to listen, that cigarettes had saved her. She was shy, excruciatingly so. She is shy still, that doesn't go away. It just gets buried under attitude. In her case, that of the trenchant and opinionated Dr Ursula Fedrigoni, authority on 14th century Italian art. The euphonious Italian name came from a teenage folly who turned into a short-lived husband. Short-lived for her, that is. Enrico had two more wives. Like all those Fedrigoni boys, he ran to fat. 'Occupational hazard,' he used to say, 'look at my dad! Proprietor of Fedrigoni's Fish 'n' Chips, king of the deep fat fryer.'

But at 17, Enrico had been a god.

At the same age, Ursula Brock couldn't open her mouth. Couldn't ask for directions, couldn't answer a question in class without blushing to her roots. Certainly couldn't enter the crowded chip shop alone with Enrico Fedrigoni behind the counter. And yet, somehow, they had got together, or he had pursued her. Why, she could never fathom. She had smoked her first cigarette with him. It tasted vile, but it was the one thing she felt they could share equally, when so much else between them seemed so imbalanced. His good looks, her pathological shyness, his ease, her complications. And when they broke up, the cigarettes bitterly sustained her, they got her through college as a late starter, and then into a doctorate.

In the days when she could smoke in the lecture hall, smoking gave her command. She could stop and light up, creating a dramatic pause to cover the little hesitation in her speech. And it was a social activity, like dancing or playing tennis, neither of which she did well, so she could share with all sorts.

Everyone happily puffing away. Together. Her tribe.

Which now includes Post-doc. She sneaks a look at him. That's a comfort fag if ever she saw one. A bad news smoke. Look at the clamp of his jaw and his eyes squinting in the smoke.

She thinks of all the people who have stood with her in this silent conspiracy. Where are they all? They can't all have died, can they? Once they used to meet in the clattery cafeteria on campus. Now they're exiled to an apron of concrete by the fire doors. She stands in a sea of fag ends; she swears she recognises every single one of them. Prufrock's coffee spoons, how are you! But she won't have a word said against cigarettes; they've defined her. Made her clear to others when she wasn't to herself.

Now who's to see her?

Only the ghost of Ursula Brock.

And now Post-doc.

She turns, determined to engage him in conversation. But she finds herself alone. How did he manage to leave without her noticing? Was he really here? Maybe she dreamt him up? Or is it the ghost of Enrico Fedrigoni she's been communing with? Enrico who's been dead for three years. The weighted fire door clicks closed and it makes her jump. Something sticks in her throat. She barks out a cough. Then another one. She can't seem to quench it. She's inhaled deeper than she realised and now she's choking on her past.

CONTRIBUTORS

AOIFE BHREATNACH is a researcher, writer and podcaster. She explores the censorship culture of twentieth-century Ireland in her podcast, Censored. Her historical writing includes *Becoming Conspicuous: Irish Travellers, Society and the State 1922-70* (2006) and several journal articles.

Is scríbhneoir dátheangach í **JULIE BREATHNACH-BANWAIT**. Tá dhá leabhar filíochta aici i gcló le Coiscéim, *Dánta Póca* agus *Ar thóir gach ní*. Beidh *Cnámha Scoilte* - cnuasach prósfhilíochta dátheangach léi — á chur i gcló i 2023.

PADDY BUSHE was born in Dublin in 1948 and now lives in Waterville, Co. Kerry. He writes in Irish and in English. His collections include *Poems With Amergin* (1989), *Digging Towards The Light* (1994), *In Ainneoin na gCloch* (2001), *Hopkins on Skellig Michael* (2001) and *The Nitpicking of Cranes* (2004).

EOIN CAHILL is from Cork. His poems have recently appeared in *Southword, Black Bough Poetry*, and *Cork Words 3*. Find him on Twitter @eoinspoems.

FIJA CALLAGHAN has been featured in podcasts, recognised by international short story competitions, and nominated for Best of the Net. Her stories can be found in venues like *Gingerbread House, Mythic Magazine, Corvid Queen*, and elsewhere. Originally from the Cascadia region, she now lives in Dublin, Ireland with her books.

EIBHLÍS CARCIONE is an award-winning bilingual poet and children's author from Cork. Her three poetry collections in Irish, *Tonn Chlíodhna* (2015), *Eala Oíche* (2019), and *Bean Róin* (2023) are published by Coiscéim. Her children's novel *Welcome to Dead Town Raven McKay* was published by Everything With Words in 2023.

DIARMUID CAWLEY is a poet and writer from Sligo, Ireland. He lectures on wine, food studies, and gastronomy in TU Dublin. His work has appeared in *The Martello, Trasna, Smashing Times, Unapologetic Magazine, Moonstone Press, Folk Life, RTÉ Brainstorm, Guzzle Magazine, The Honest Ulsterman, Poetry Jukebox* and *The Irish Times*.

SIMON COSTELLO's poems have appeared in *The Poetry Review, The Stinging Fly, New England Review, The London Magazine, Bath Magg* among others. His debut pamphlet *Saturn Devouring* will be published by The Lifeboat press in 2023.

MARTINA DALTON lives in Tramore, County Waterford. Her poem *Wedding Dress* won the Listowel Writers' Week Poem of the Year at the An Post Irish Book Awards 2022. Her publication credits include *The Irish Times* and the *Irish Independent's New Irish Writing, Poetry Ireland Review, The Stinging Fly*, and *Rattle*.

EILÍN DE PAOR lives in Dublin. Her poems have appeared in *The Stony Thursday Book, Banshee, Skylight 47, 14, Abridged* and *Raleigh Review*, among others. Her pamphlet, *In the Jitterfritz of Neon*, a collaboration with Damien B. Donnelly, was published by The Hedgehog Poetry Press. Twitter & Linktree: @edepaor

PATRICK DEELEY's tenth collection, *Dancing Still*, will appear from Dedalus Press in 2024. His critically acclaimed memoir, *The Hurley Maker's Son*, was a bestseller in 2016. His awards for writing include the Lawrence O'Shaughnessy Award, the Eilis Dillon Award, and the Dermot Healy Poetry Prize.

THEODORE DEPPE is the author of seven books of poems. His most recent collection is *Riverlight* (Arlen House, 2019). His work has received a Pushcart Prize and has appeared in *Poetry Ireland Review, The Stinging Fly, Cyphers, Poetry, Kenyon Review* and elsewhere. He lives in Connemara.

DAMIEN B. DONNELLY is the author of 2 pamphlets, a micro-collection and full collection, *Enough!* published by Hedgehog. He's the host of Eat the Storms poetry podcast and editor-in-chief of *The Storms* journal. His work appears in various anthologies and his 2nd collection arrives with Turas Press in 2024.

RORY DUFFY's work has appeared in a number of journals including *Southword, Crannog, Skylight 47, Boyne Berries, The Stony Thursday Book,* & *A New Ulster*. Winner Red Line Poetry 2019, nominated for The Forward Prize 2020. Runner up in the Trocaire/Poetry Ireland 2022. He also writes short fiction.

BARBARA DUNNE is a poet, painter and print-maker living in Connemara Co. Galway with her children and three cats. Her poetry has been published in *Crannóg, The Martello Journal, The Storms Journal* as well as in other Irish and international journals. She is currently editing her first collection of poetry.

Proud Cork man **ALAN EGAN** is fascinated by his city's history and the array of characters who daily walk its streets. After "retirement" Alan went to UCC, acquired primary and master's degrees, became a tutor, began to write, and many of these stories have been published locally, nationally and internationally.

FRANK FARRELLY is from Waterford. He won the Rush Poetry Prize, Fingal Poetry Prize, and The Francis Ledwidge Award. His work has appeared in *Poetry Ireland Review, Southword, The Moth, The Stinging Fly,* and other magazines. His first collection, *The Boiler Room* (Revival Press) was published in 2020.

MATTHEW GEDEN was born in England, moving to Kinsale, County Cork, in 1990. His most recent collection is *The Cloud Architect* (Doire Press, 2022). He was Writer in Residence for Cork County Library and Arts Service 2020-23.

ELIZABETH GIBSON is based in Manchester. Her poetry has appeared in *Confingo, Impossible Archetype, Lighthouse, Magma, Popshot, The Storms*, and *Under the Radar*. In 2021, she received a DYCP grant from Arts Council England, and in 2023 she undertook a paid zine-making residency with Manchester Poetry Library. https://elizabeth-gibson.com. Twitter/Instagram: @Grizonne.

SONYA GILDEA is winner of the John McGahern Literature Award and the Cúirt International New Writer's Award. She is a Poetry Ireland Introductions poet and recipient of an Arts Council Literature Bursary Award. She has published in *The Stinging Fly, Tolka, New Irish Writing, The Common, The Cormorant Broadsheet, Crannog*, and various anthologies.

EVA H.D. wrote *Rotten Perfect Mouth, The Natural Hustle*, and the short film *Jackals & Fireflies*.

SUE HANN's debut memoir-in-essays is forthcoming with Neem Tree Press. She is a London Writers Awards recipient 2019-20 and winner of the Diana Woods Memorial Award 2020. You can find her at suehannwrites.com and on Instagram @SueHannwrites

DARA HIGGINS lives in the rain and fog of Ireland's east coast with his family and many cats. He spent the last few decades writing for television and playing bass guitar and has very little to show for it.

ELEANOR HOOKER's third poetry collection *Of Ochre and Ash* (Dedalus Press) is the recipient of the 2022 Michael Hartnett Award. *Where Memory Lies* (Bonnefant Press), her Markievicz Award book, was published August 2023. Eleanor is a PhD candidate at the University of Limerick. She is an RNLI lifeboat helm. www.eleanorhooker.com

AILEEN HUNT is a Dublin writer with a particular interest in flash forms and creative nonfiction. Her work has appeared in various online and print journals including *Craft, Sweet Lit, The Four Faced Liar, Hippocampus*, and *The Ogham Stone*. You can find her at aileen-hunt.com and @HuntAileen

ROSEMARY JOHNSTON's novella, *Source*, won the New Fictions Prize. Her stories and poetry have appeared in British and Irish magazines. Her non-fiction piece, *The Rocky Road*, was longlisted for the Fish Memoir Prize. She is the editor of *The Vixen* magazine. She is from Belfast, but is based in Yorkshire.

Recent poems by **FIN KEEGAN** appear in *Swerve* and *Amsterdam Quarterly*; other poems were shortlisted this year for the Bournemouth Writing Prize and Fish Poetry Prize. Articles: *Irish Arts Review, Irish Times* and *Dublin Review of Books*. A story, *Remembering Albert*, was broadcast on the BBC World Service in 1998.

PHIL KINGSTON works in community engagement. He has written for stage and television as well as working as an actor and facilitator. He work appears in *Dogs Singing* (Salmon Press), *The Stony Thursday Book* (Limerick Arts Office) and online in the *Poets Directory*. He was one of Poetry Ireland's Introductions 2022.

Is file dátheangach í **CAITRÍONA LANE** a bhfuil cónaí uirthi i gConamara. Bhain sí an gearrliosta amach i 2023 don duais Eavan Boland Emerging Poet Award. Roghnaigh Éigse Éireann dánta dá cuid don tsraith Céadlínte 2022. Tá a cuid saothair foilsithe ag *Aneas, Comhar, Feasta, The Echo, Galway Review* agus eile.

SHAUNNA LEE LYNCH is a writer and performer from Cork. She writes tongue-in-cheek poems, intended to be spoken. Shaunna has performed her work at arts festivals around Ireland and abroad, and in 2019, she won the All-Ireland Poetry Slam Competition. She also writes for theatre and film.

KEVIN MACALAN lives in rural Co Waterford. He has an MA in Creative Writing, is a founding member of the West Waterford Arts Group, and recently contributed to *An Áitiúil*, published by The Madrigal Press and The Martello Journal. Kevin edited the novel *The Aoife Effect* written by Eamonn Cooney.

GRACE MAGEE is a horror writer and editor based in Belfast. She's been previously published in *Sublunary Review, All Existing, Awkward Middle Children*, and others. She is on Twitter @grace_e_magee

Is file, drámadóir agus aistritheoir é **EOIN MC EVOY**. Is é Comhstiúrthóir AerachAiteachGaelach é in éineacht le Ciara Ní É. Roghnaíodh Eoin do scéim Poetry Ireland Introductions 2021 agus tá saothair dá chuid le léamh in *Comhar, Trumpet, The Stinging Fly, Cyphers, Feasta* agus *Aneas* (le teacht).

DAVID MCLOGHLIN is a poet and writer of creative nonfiction. His books are *Waiting For Saint Brendan and Other Poems* and *Santiago Sketches. CRASH CENTRE* will be published by Salmon in May 2024. He teaches creative writing with Writers in Schools, and is a mentor with the National Mentoring Scheme.

CONOR MONTAGUE is from Galway. His debut collection of short fiction, *Capital Vices*, will be published by Reflex Press in Autumn 2023.

MARY MORRISSY is the author of three novels, *Mother of Pearl, The Pretender* and *The Rising of Bella Casey* and two collections of short stories, *A Lazy Eye* and *Prosperity Drive*. Her fourth novel, *Penelope Unbound*, has just been published with Banshee Press. A member of Aosdána, she was formerly the Associate Director of Creative Writing at UCC.

Agallamh sa Cheo-Cnoc Bhréanainn, a ghnóthaigh Gradam Mícheál Ó hAirtnéide 2021, is ea an cnuasach dánta is úra ó pheann **CEAITÍ NÍ BHEILDIÚIN** agus an ceathrú cnuasach dá chuid filíochta foilsithe ag Coiscéim. Rogha dánta óna saothair maille le haistriúcháin go Béarla, ó Paddy Bushe, atá i *Lig don nGiorria Suí/Let the Hare Sit*, Dedalus Press 2022.

Tógadh **ÚNA NIC CÁRTHAIGH** i gCloch na gCoillte in Iarthar Chorcaí agus tá sí ag cur fuithí anois sa Ghaillimh. Bhain sí BA sa Chumarsáid amach le hOllscoil na Gaillimhe agus Máistir Gairmiúil san Oideachas ó Choláiste Mhuire Gan Smál. Tá suim faoi leith aici i ngearrscéalta, splancfhicsean agus filíocht i nGaeilge.

Tógadh **LAOIGHSEACH NÍ CHOISTEALBHA** i gceantair an Lagáin in oirthear Dhún na nGall, ach tá cónaí uirthi i nGaillimh ó 2012. Tá sí ag cur fúithi anois i gConamara Theas. Tá an chéad chnuasach filíochta, Solas Geimhridh, ar na bacáin.

Scríobhann **RÉALTÁN NÍ LEANNÁIN** idir fhilíocht, phrós agus dhrámaí raidió. Tá liosta de chuid dá saothar ar a blag, http://turasailse. blogspot.com/ Cuireann sí an podchraoladh https://blath-na-dtulach. com/ i láthair.

ELIZABETH O'CONNELL-THOMPSON is a poet living in Chicago. She is the author of the chapbook *Honorable Mention*, and her work has been published in *Iron Horse Literary Review, Newcity, Poetry Ireland Review*, and *Portland Review*, among others. An associate editor for *RHINO*, she cohosts the RHINO Reads Series.

Rugadh agus tógadh **SEOSAMH Ó FÁTHARTA** i gceantar Chois Fharraige i gConamara. Faoi láthair oibríonn sé mar oibrí tógála. Caitheann sé a chuid ama saor ag léamh agus ag streachailt lena chuid scríbhneoireachta féin. Na scríbhneoirí is mó a chuaigh i bhfeidhm air ná Borges, Schulz agus an Cadhanach, ar ndóigh.

ALANNA OFFIELD is a disabled, queer, Chicana from New Mexico now living in the north of Ireland. Her poetry has appeared in *Abridged, Cyphers, Rust+Moth, Porridge Mag*, and other publications. She completed an MA in Poetry at Queen's University Belfast. She owns Seaside Books, an independent online and traveling bookshop.

JAMIE O'HALLORAN won first place in Southword's 2023 Subscriber Competition and first runner up in the 2023 Mairtín Crawford Award. Her *Corona Connemara & Half a Crown* was a winner in the 2021 Fool for Poetry Chapbook Competition. She lives in Connemara and is working on a first collection.

Is as Béal Feirste é **SEÁN Ó MUIREAGÁIN**. Scríobhann sé filíocht, amhráin, gearrscéalta agus tá sé san am i láthair ag tabhairt fá úrscéal. Bhí sé ariamh ag gníomh ar son phobal na Gaeilge ar fud na tíre seo, sa Ghaeltacht agus sa Ghalltacht. Tá dúil mhór aige sa cheol ghaelach agus is iomaí oíche a chaith sé le lucht ragairne ag ceol is ag cóisireacht nó ag cleamaireacht le Cleamairí Feirste.

BRIAN O'SULLIVAN teaches English at St. Mary's College of Maryland. His work has appeared in *Rattle, ONE ART, The Galway Review* and other journals, and he is a reader for *Chestnut Review*. He was born in Queens, New York to parents from Kanturk and Adrigole in County Cork.

MAGGIE SAWKINS recently hosted an episode of BBC Radio 4's *Tongue and Talk: The Dialect Poets*. She is the recipient of a Ted Hughes Award for New Work in Poetry for her live literature production *Zones of Avoidance. The House Where Courage Lives* (Waterloo Press) is her latest collection. www.hookedonwords.me

COLM SCULLY from Cork has recently been published in *Poetry Ireland Review, Cyphers* and *The Friday Poem*. He is a poetry filmmaker and his films have won prizes internationally, including the Deanna Tulley Multimedia Prize 2022. You can learn more at colmscully.com

MICHAEL SHEEHAN is originally from Limerick and now lives in Cork, where he works for the Irish Prison Service. His work has been previously published in *The SHOP, Southword, Revival,* and the *Irish Examiner*.

JANET SHEPPERSON is a poet and fiction writer based in Belfast. Short stories published widely, with 2 shortlisted for Hennessy Awards. Poetry collections include *THE APHRODITE STONE* (Salmon Poetry) and *EVE COMPLAINS TO GOD* (Lagan Press). Her novel *VINNY'S WILDERNESS* was published in 2016 by Liberties Press.

ANNE TANNAM has written three poetry collections, the latest *Twenty-six Letters of a New Alphabet* (Salmon Poetry 2021). She is working on a fourth collection thanks to an Arts Council of Ireland Literature Bursary. Anne is Poetry Ireland's current Poet in Residence. For more on Anne's poetry, visit www.annetannampoetry.ie.

FIONA TRACEY is a poet from West Virginia. She earned her BA in Creative Writing from Shepherd University and is pursuing an MA in Creative Writing at UCC. Her poems explore place and identity and have appeared in *The Naugatuck River Review, Orchards Poetry Journal*, and *The Stonecoast Review*.

Is ó Pharóiste an Fheirtéaraigh i gCorca Dhuibhne d' **EIBHLÍN UÍ IARLAITHE**, iar mhúinteoir scoile atá ag cumadh filíochta, ag scríobh scéalta beaga agus ag cumadh lúibíní agus agallaimh beirte ó 2008.Tá dhá chnuasach filíochta *Na Buataisí Buí* agus *Mo Ghúna Síoda Buí* agus sé leabhar sa tsraith *Orla Uan* foilsithe aici go dtí seo.

DANIEL WADE is a writer from Dublin. In January 2017, his play *The Collector* was staged at the New Theatre. He is also the author of the poetry collections *Iceberg Relief* (Underground Voices, 2017), *Rapids* (Finishing Line Press, 2021), and the novel *A Land Without Wolves* (Temple Dark Books, 2021).

JEMMA WALSH is an Irish poet based in London. She is a graduate of Russian and Classics from Trinity College Dublin. She is currently doing a Masters in Creative and Life Writing at Goldsmiths College. Her work has been published in *The Irish Times, Moth Magazine, Crossways Magazine* and elsewhere.

MARY WILKINSON is a published writer of fiction, non-fiction and poetry. She has written for radio and is a Pushcart Prize nominee. Her novella, *Quotidian*, is published with Reflex Press. She lives in Galway.